Subscribers

J K Almond, Eston, Teesside
J M Almond, Warkworth, Northumberland
J Ambler, Wisborough Green, West Sussex
Archive Bookshop, Lydney, Gloucestershire
R Bade, Morden, Surrey
Dr T B Bagenal, Lane Head, Gunnerside
J L Barker, Healaugh, Yorkshire
T Barr, Mitcham, Surrey
Dr B M J Barton, Corby, Lincolnshire
S Bassham, Ribblehead, Yorkshire
C Beech, Hurst, Richmond
R A Belson, Hellesdon, Norwich
J S Bennett, Warrington, Cheshire
D Borthwick, Gateshead, Tyne & Wear
I Boulton, Boldon Colliery, South Tyneside
S & T Bridges, Ovington, Northumberland
R Bridgwood, Torquay, Devon
P A Brooks, Duffield, Derbyshire
Dr I J Brown, Wakefield
M J Burrow, Rothwell, Leeds
R Burt, Newton St Cyres, Devon
M C Cawthorne, Westhoughton, Lancs
M G Charlton, Newcastle upon Tyne
P Claughton, Pembrokeshire
P Clayton, Wolverhampton
R Collinge, Luddenden, Halifax
R Cook, Nelson, Lancashire
R & C Cork, Ashbourne
D Cranstone, Gateshead
S Croft, Rookhope, Durham
J J Croston, Standish, Wigan
Dr D Dalrymple-Smith, Baslow, Derbyshire
D W Dalton, Leyburn, North Yorkshire
P Deakin, Trentham, Staffs
D C Dean, Cliviger, Lancs
E Dennison, Beverley, East Yorkshire
E M Dixon, Belper, Derbyshire
G Dobbs, Beverley, East Yorkshire
J M Dobbs, Slaley, Hexham
Dr I Drummond, Davyhulme, Manchester
T W Evans, Merthyr Tydfil
M Flux, Leyburn, North Yorkshire
I & P Forbes, Weardale
J R Foster-Smith, Middleton-in-Teesdale, Co Durham
T Fretwell, Bishop Auckland
M Gale, Witham, Essex
R Gosling, Alveston, Gloucestershire
D M Goth, Hornby, Lancaster
D Gough, Newthorpe, Notts
P Greaves, Bonsall
E M Green, Twickenham, Middlesex
F Harris, Cheltenham
P R Hart, Carleton-in-Craven, North Yorkshire
A H Hawkins, Mollington, Chester
Dr W F Heyes, Middleton-in-Teesdale
M Higgins, Doncaster, South Yorkshire
P Hodge, Hebden, North Yorkshire
R N Holden, Stockport, Cheshire
R P Holdsworth, Leeds
S C Holt, Newark, Notts
B M Hunt, Nelson, Lancs
E L Hurt, Bulwell, Nottingham
R J Ireland, Leyland, Lancashire
P Jackson, Billingham
B Jones, Northallerton, North Yorkshire
I C Kerr, Bridgnorth, Shropshire
D F King, Northallerton, North Yorkshire
J A Knight, London
Dr J A Knight, Shirland, Derbyshire
R Lamb, Beverley, East Yorkshire

Land Quality Management Ltd, University of Nottingham
C C Lansdell, Norwich, Norfolk
J Lawson, Castle Douglas, Dumphries & Galloway
D Lawton, Longley, Huddersfield
D Lowde, Wellow, Notts
Mike Luff, Coalville, Leicestershire
Dr W J Lumb, Arkengarthdale, North Riding of Yorkshire
R T McAndrew, Hartlepool
D J McCurdy, Golborne, Lancs
J MacPherson, Linthorpe, Middlesborough
K Makin, Todmorden, Lancs
S Maslauskas, Mayfield, Ashbourne
A F Mills, Clayton West, Yorkshire
S Mitchell, Silsden, West Yorkshire
Mike Moore Books, Church Aston, Shropshire
J H Morris, Porthmadog
D Moss, Whitby, North Yorkshire
Dr S Murphy, Crook, Kendal
Dr J O Myers, Austwick, North Yorkshire
National Museums & Galleries of Wales, Library
W E E Nicholas, Bardsey, West Yorkshire
North Yorkshire Record Office, Northallerton
R Nuttall, Belfast
Dr C B Oxby, Leeds, Yorkshire
W J D Parkhouse, Coleford, Gloucestershire
J R Peacock, Worsthorne, Lancashire
F Peel, Ellastone
D Poole, Rawdon, Yorkshire
C L M Porter, Ashbourne
M Potts, Nottingham
Dr C Pounder, Cotmanhay, Derbyshire
R A Richardson, Longridge, Lancashire
Dr J H Rieuwerts, Sheffield
I G Roberts, Bradford, West Yorkshire
M Roe, Queensbury, Bradford
P Roe, Swaledale
Prof. W A S Sarjeant, Saskatoon, Canada
L Mason Scarr, Bainbridge, North Yorkshire
S Sharp, Harpenden, Herts
R Shaw, Aylestone, Leicester
R L Shepherdson, Newcastle upon Tyne
Dr W Slatcher, Rochdale
P J Smith, Bugthorpe, York
Dr R Smith, Cold Ash, Newbury, Berks
R A Snowball, Fakenham, Norfolk
R A Stewart, Middleton-St-George
G H Stott, Harden, Bingley
A Suddes, Darlington
Dr J Suter, Leeds, West Yorkshire
Wes Taylor, Walton-on-Trent
A J Thorogood, Virginia Water, Surrey
Threlkeld Mining Museum, Cumbria
K Turner, Blackburn
R W Turton, Newark, Nottinghamshire
R Vernon, Walton, Wakefield
A Waggett, Epworth, North Lincs
Dr T M Whitaker, Low Bentham, Yorks
R F White, Northallerton, North Yorkshire
D Wilcock, Bowburn, Durham
C J Williams, Marford, Wrexham
D Williams, Tideswell, Derbyshire
I A Williamson, Ambleside, Cumbria
Dr L Willies, Matlock Bath, Derbyshire
R V Willan, Kendal, Cumbria
F C Wilson, Durham
G Wolstencroft, Macclesfield
J Wood, Winster, Derbyshire
S Woodbridge, Marlow, Bucks
G Wybranski, Shipley, West Yorkshire

Northern Mine Research Society

The Northern Mine Research Society is dedicated to the preservation and recording of mining history, with northern referring to the Society's administrative base rather than its field of interest. With over 400 members, it is one of Britain's largest mining history organisations.

Generally members are encouraged to follow their own pursuits, but can be introduced to others sharing the same field of interest.

Members enjoy the following facilities:-

FIELD MEETINGS - a programme of both surface and underground meetings is annually arranged, with various venues throughout the mining areas of Britain.

PUBLICATIONS - The high quality publications produced by the Society have the general series title of 'British Mining'. Usually a Monograph and a Memoirs are issued annually to each full member. A Monograph, as the name suggests, is a complete and authoritative dissertation on one mine or area, whereas the Memoirs contain a selection of members' researches into various mines, miners, techniques and so forth. The Society strongly encourages members to contribute to these publications, which now lead the field in British mining history.

THE NEWSLETTER - is issued quarterly and provides a medium for members to exchange ideas and information, to bring news of mining events, past and present. It also contains reviews of newly published books, society events etc and carries short articles of general interest.

THE RECORDS - are available for research purposes and consist of original documents, membersí reports, plans, maps, photographs etc. which are continually being added to by donations from many sources. The comprehensive indexing of these records is an on-going project, with files being organised on a county and parish basis. In addition, there are indexes to specific sites. The collection is especially strong on Yorkshire material, but other counties are also represented. The Recorder will be pleased to arrange for the above items to be available to members for consultation on request.

THE LIBRARY - containing a wide range of books, pamphlets and similar literature related to Britain's extractive industries is at the disposal of all members. This service is constantly being enlarged by the Society and also by donations from outside.

If you are concerned with industrial archaeology, geology, local/technical/mining history, or are simply fascinated by old mines, the Society cordially invites you to take up membership.

Enquiries should be addressed to:-

Northern Mine Research Society,
38 Main Street,
Sutton in Craven,
KEIGHLEY
Yorkshire,
BD20 7HD

SWALEDALE

• its Mines and Smelt Mills •

Michael Gill

Landmark Publishing

Published by
Landmark Publishing Ltd,
Ashbourne Hall, Ashbourne, Derbyshire DE6 1EJ, England
Tel: (01335) 347349 Fax: (01335) 347303
e-mail: landmark@clara.net
web site: www.landmarkpublishing.co.uk

British Library Cataloguing in Publication Data

ISBN 1-84306-018-3

© Michael Gill

Printed in Great Britain by MPG Ltd, Bodmin, Cornwall
Design: Ashley J Emery/Michael Gill
Cover: James Allsopp

Front cover: Marrick High and Low smelt mills
Back cover: Bunting Level-tips, smithy and house teams, 1976

CONTENTS

WEIGHTS AND DATES

Before 1752, when the calendar was changed, New Year's Day fell on Lady Day (March 25th). For ease of reading, therefore, all January to March dates, from before the change, have all been written as if New Year's Day had fallen on January 1st.

A few specialised mining terms have been used, and their meaning is given in the glossary, but wherever possible these have been avoided. Depths were usually referred to in fathoms, which equal six feet. Lead was weighed in fothers (fodders) and ore in horse loads, which were 22 cwts and 2 cwts respectively. These have been left unchanged in quotations, but converted to tons (2240 lbs) elsewhere.

INTRODUCTION

My interest in the Swaledale mines began at Whitsuntide 1966 on a Northern Cavern & Mine Research Society field meet. Visits to the Surrender and Old Gang Smelt Mills, plus a walk up Gunnerside Gill and a trip to the Sir Francis Level engines left me hooked.

This interest endured during the 1970s, when I was active in the southern parts of the Dales, but was rekindled with a vengeance in the 1980s by the painstaking work of my good friend Les Tyson. His willingness to discuss this work in detail meant that, for the first time, our understanding of lead mining was being seriously and systematically re-examined, though both of us obviously owe a great debt to Robert Clough, Bernard Jennings and Arthur Raistrick for their pioneering work on the subject.

Readers can be forgiven for asking why there is this fascination with a long dead industry. I would reply as follows. Firstly, there is the personal pleasure of fitting more pieces into a complex jigsaw puzzle to gain a better understanding of the area's mining industry, its ups and downs, the principal, and sometimes the lesser, players. Secondly, a more complete understanding of the Dale's principal industry leads to a better understanding of the wider story of the Dale's development.

After so much effort in studying the available archives, some might argue that we are approaching the limit of our knowledge in some areas. I am, however, optimistic that this is not so. A new generation of mining historians, with archæological and other analytical skills, is already getting established. They will look at the remains, both on the surface and underground, and raise new questions. In time, aspects of my own work will be questioned, just as I have questioned that of others. I eagerly look forward to that time.

CONSOLIDATION WORK

Since the 1950s most of the structures associated with lead mining and smelting in the Yorkshire Dales have deteriorated significantly, but a few have been consolidated by the Yorkshire Dales National Park Authority, English Heritage and the Earby Mines Research Group. All this reflects the growing interest in all aspects of the lead industry, not least in much needed archaeological field work.

PREVIOUS PUBLICATIONS

Robert Clough's architectural study of *The Lead Smelting Mills of the Yorkshire Dales* was published in 1962, but the field work for it was done in the late 1940s and the 1950s, when many mills were fairly complete. By that time, memories of the industry were fading and, as a result, Clough's text has many deficiencies. Nevertheless, for all its faults, his book remains the only comprehensive survey of Yorkshire's smelt mills.

Although never published and, therefore, difficult for many to get hold of, Bernard Jenning's thesis remains a major study of the area's mining industry. Fortunately, the section on lead mining in Fieldhouse &

Jennings' book *A History of Richmond and Swaledale* drew heavily on the thesis. This book is recommended as the best general history of the area.

Arthur Raistrick's two books on *The Lead Industry of Wensleydale and Swaledale*, which were published in 1975, made the first serious attempt to establish a time-frame for the industry. This model stood unchallenged until the early 1990s, when it was becoming clear that changes, some of them major, were needed.

In the 1990s, therefore, the Northern Mine Research Society's *British Mining* series published monographs on the mines of Marrick, Grinton and Arkengarthdale by Les Tyson. The same series also has a growing number of papers on aspects of mining and smelting in Swaledale. Of particular importance were a reassessment of the London Lead Company's supposed involvement in Swaledale during the 18th century, and papers on "Yorkshire Smelting Mills" and the Marske Mines. These led to the rejection of many old assumptions and to the emergence of new interpretations.

Faced with this body of published material on the subject, anyone new to it is, therefore, faced with a series of confusing statements on the dates and sometimes the locations of mines and smelt mills. This book draws on that new work and seeks to present it in an accessible way.

ACKNOWLEDGEMENTS

The writer is pleased to acknowledge the help given to him by the following organisations and their staff, as well as individuals: Brotherton Library – University of Leeds, Durham County Record Office, Gateshead Library, Northern Mine Research Society Records, North Yorkshire County Record Office, Oxford University Museum of Natural History, Public Record Office, Warwickshire County Record Office, York Minster Library, Yorkshire Dales National Park Authority, Lawrence Barker, Roger Burt, David & Margaret Carlisle, Nigel Chapman, the late Robert Clough, David Cranstone, Anna Davies, Ed Dennison, the late Michael Dickinson, Edmund Green, Bernard Jennings, Barry Jones, Richard Lamb, Hazel Martell, the late Arthur Raistrick, Martin Roe, Susan Sharp, Richard Smith, Ian Spensley, Les Tyson, Robert White.

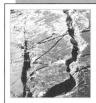

FINDING THE ORE

The geological structure of the Yorkshire Dales may be summarised as alternating layers of hard and soft sedimentary rocks which were laid down during the Carboniferous period, between 350 and 270 million years ago. The characteristic rock-types are limestone, sandstone, flagstone and shale, with lead ore being found mostly in the first two. These once horizontal sediments were arched upwards, to form the Pennine anticline, and further disturbed by faulting. The anticline's core is formed of massive limestone which, unlike that of the Peak District of Derbyshire, is almost unmineralised. This core is overlain by alternating layers of chert, limestone, shale and sandstone, called the Yoredale Series. Most of the lead ore came from these rocks, with the Main and the Underset Limestones, together with their associated cherts, being the richest horizons in Swaledale and Arkengarthdale.

The following figure gives the average thickness of the beds, but it must be remembered that this may vary, sometimes over short distances.

Metallic ores were usually found in near vertical fault fissures, called veins. These varied in width from a few inches to many feet, being usually narrowest in softer rocks, such as shale. They were filled with gangue minerals, which included clay and sand, as well as fluorspar (calcium fluoride), calcite (calcium carbonate) and barytes (barium sulphate). The lead miners discarded these as worthless, but in the 20th century barytes and a little fluorspar were recovered from the old dumps because uses for them had been developed.

The lead ore (galena = lead sulphide) was

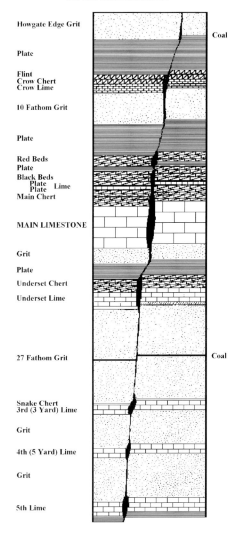

TYPICAL GEOLOGICAL SECTION IN SWALEDALE

Howgate Edge Grit
Coal
Plate
Flint
Crow Chert
Crow Lime
10 Fathom Grit
Plate
Red Beds
Plate
Black Beds
Plate
Plate   Lime
Main Chert
MAIN LIMESTONE
Grit
Plate
Underset Chert
Underset Lime
27 Fathom Grit
Coal
Snake Chert
3rd (3 Yard) Lime
Grit
4th (5 Yard) Lime
Grit
5th Lime

found in distinct 'ribs', which ran through the vein, or it was mixed with the gangue. Sphalerite (blende = zinc sulphide) was usually found with the galena. Although it was never worked commercially in Swaledale, blende was difficult to remove from lead concentrates. Mineralisation was not uniform, and those parts of a vein where the ore was richest were called ore-shoots. These were usually found against sandstone or limestone, where the vein had a small vertical displacement or throw. Dales' ore-shoots were, therefore, often restricted to short distances vertically, but could be extensive laterally. This contrasted with areas of metamorphic and igneous rocks, like Cornwall, where tin and copper ore-shoots were often over 1000 feet deep.

The unpredictability of ore shoots encouraged miners to continue their exploratory works in the, often futile, hope of riches to come. All mining areas have tales, some of which can be substantiated, of such trials being abandoned, having broken the company involved, only to be restarted by a new company, which found ore after driving just a few feet further.

Another type of ore-shoot, called a flot or float, has been found, especially on the south side of Swaledale between Grinton and Spout Gill. Here the mineralisation has spread sideways from the vein along bedding planes or even caverns in the limestone. The ore in these flots was often found with very little gangue and was sometimes very rich, but limited in extent.

There have been many theories as to how the lead veins were formed. Geologists now believe that very hot and highly saline solutions (six or more times more saline than sea water) flowed into the region through sandstone aquifers. In Swaledale, for example, it is thought that the sandstone between the Main and Underset Limestones may have carried the fluids, which also contained sulphides of lead, zinc, copper, barium and fluorine. As they found their way into the limestone through fault fissures, these brines cooled and the various minerals crystallised to form veins.

The highest mineralised formation in Swaledale was the Crow Limestone and its overlying chert, together about 27 feet thick. They are at the base of a series of thin layers of limestone and chert, separated by bands of shale, called the Crow Beds. The first workings at Blakethwaite, at the head of Gunnerside Gill, were in this bed. Below the Crow Beds were the Ten Fathom Grit, which was generally poor for lead, and a thick bed of shale.

Most of the lead ore came from the Main Limestone and the Main Chert immediately above it, which are around 72 and 18 feet thick respectively. Some ore was also won from the Little Limestone, and from two beds of chert (the Black and Red Beds) above that.

	Average thickness	
	ft	ins
Red Bed	15	0
Shale	7	0
Black Bed	34	0
Shale	0	8
Little Limestone	4	0
Shale	0	8
Main Chert	17	9
Main Limestone	72	9

The Underset Limestone (25' 6") and Chert (27' 9") were separated from the Main Limestone by around 55 feet of generally barren sandstone and shale. The Underset beds were usually very productive of lead ore, but they were much thinner than the Main beds and were, therefore, exhausted more quickly.

The beds below the Undersets generally held little lead. They begin with the 27 Fathom Grit which, like the Ten Fathom Grit, seldom carried much lead ore. In places, the grit was associated with a thin bed of coal.

Below the 27 Fathom Grit are three thin beds of limestone, which the miners called the 3rd, 4th and 5th Limes. They are now called the Three Yard, Five Yard and the Middle Limestones respectively, and are separated by sandstone and shale. These limestones, which were generally much too deep to work, were tried from the Engine Sump in Sir Francis Level, and at Fryer Intake Mine, near Low Row. They were also worked at Keld Heads Mine, in Wensleydale. Deposits of lead ore were found at all these places, but, owing to the thinness of the beds, were soon worked out.

Small amounts of copper ore have been found around the edge of the Swaledale - Wensleydale orefield. It has been worked at Feldom, East Layton, Billybanks (near Richmond) and around Middleton Tyas. In the latter place, it was fairly important for a while in the 18th century. A copper vein has also been tried at the head of Great Sleddale.

Thin seams of coal are found throughout the Yoredale Series, which were deposited in a shallow sea. From time to time the sea level fell, allowing swamps and forests to flourish and form peat. When sea levels rose, this peat was covered by other sediments and eventually became coal. The thickness of these seams is variable, but they were widely worked, particularly for use in limekilns. One seam, near the base of the Millstone Grit, has been extensively worked at Tan Hill, after which it is named. The Tan Hill Coal occurs near the summits of most hills in the area and

has been worked from great numbers of shallow shafts and a few levels.

Aerial view of the Scatter Scar and North Rake Hushes (YDNPA, 1989)

MINING THE ORE

The first miners worked ore wherever veins outcropped, either in cliffs or in rock with a shallow soil cover. Once a vein's direction had been found, however, it could easily be followed by digging trenches or sinking pits either across or along its expected course. Not all prospecting trenches are of this antiquity, however, as, for example, the Old Gang Mining Company dug several at Brownsey End in 1871.

As lead mining developed during mediæval times, many mineral owners allowed partnerships of miners, which often included wealthy local men, to work blocks of ground in return for a fraction of all the ore raised. Such mining ground was measured in units called meers, which in Swaledale were 30 yards along the vein and 7½ yards (the quarter cord) on either side of it, giving room to sink a shaft, make spoil heaps and dressing heaps and erect a small building or coe. Elsewhere in the dales, meers varied in length from 30 to 32 or even 42 yards.

These early miners worked their veins from shafts, often less than 100 feet deep, which was about as deep as could be easily wound using a jack-roll. The workings from such shafts may, however, have been considerably deeper than 100 feet owing to the use of stepped shafts. As early as 1631, for example, some mines in Derbyshire had reached depths of 240 feet by sinking a series of vertical steps of between 50 and 60 feet, separated by sidesteps of around 20 feet. In order to make haulage easier and to improve ventilation, new shafts were sunk at regular intervals. This has left lines of shafts, sometimes incorrectly called bell-pits, along the course of each vein.

Another form of mining, which was used at various times for both prospecting for veins and working them, was hushing. This was a form of opencast mining used in hilly, unpopulated places because it caused considerable damage and washed rock into nearby becks. To make a hush, first a reservoir was built above the place to be tried. It was then breached to release a torrent of water which tore up the soil and exposed the underlying rock and any veins. A hush's course could be changed by using trenches, or gutters, to divert the water. Once found, veins were worked by quarrying techniques, with hushing only being used to flush out debris periodically. Some large open-cuts were also called hushes, but there is little evidence that they were ever systematically worked by water. Some of the large hushes in Arkengarthdale have a complex series of water courses and dams associated with them and the precise way in which they were worked is not yet understood.

Clearly, hushing could not be used where veins were split into meers because neighbouring miners would have been endangered. There is evidence that this method tended to be used when a vein was considered to have been worked out using traditional mining techniques. For example, in June 1767 Adam Birch and partners were granted 300 yards by 40 yards quarter cord at Merryfield, with the proviso that:

"They are to work the said strip in the mineral way, but the Old Vein by hushing, or in the mineral way."

The term *"mineral way"* means mining by shafts, levels etc, whereas the option to work the Old Vein by hushing suggests that it was considered to be practically worked out. At Lownathwaite, however, plans dating from the late 18th century show myriad shafts where the North and South Hushes now are. The latter hushes are thought to date from the first two or three decades of the 19th century. They were worked again later, but probably not by hushing. This reflects practice elsewhere, where hushes or opencasts were made after considerable earlier mining. Arkengarthdale has two areas of well developed hushing, one on Mould Side, which includes the Hungry, Dodgson, Turf Moor and Cobbler Hushes, and the other in Slei Gill, which includes the Tanner Rake, Scatter Scar, North Rake and Fell End Hushes.

As the 18th century progressed, miners were obliged to sink deeper, usually vertical, shafts which were wound by horse whims. Because of the investment needed, the workings from such shafts were much more extensive and they were, therefore, spread much more thinly across mined areas.

Because many veins in Swaledale and Arkengarthdale were cut by steep-sided valleys, it was easy to drive drainage tunnels or adits into them. The earliest of these drains, which were around 3' 6" high by 1' 6" wide, were already extensive by the end of the 17th century. From the late 18th century, however, such levels were driven large enough (6' 6" high by 4' 6" wide) and straight enough to be fitted with a narrow gauge railway on which horses pulled wheeled waggons. Such horse levels, as they were known, meant that a number of veins could be worked from one place and led to the concentration of dressing floors at level mouths.

If all went according to plan, when a level reached the vein, it was at or near the bottom of the bed it was intended to work in. Because, however, the ore was found in certain beds of limestone, and these were disrupted by faulting, no one level was sufficient for working any given area. As a result, the hillsides are peppered with levels at all horizons.

When ore was found in workable amounts, the miners would systematically remove it in a process known as stoping. This left a void, called a stope, which they would often stow with waste rock in order to save the cost of taking it to the surface. Where ore was thought likely to be present either above or below the level, vertical shafts, called rises or sumps, were driven respectively upwards or downwards in search of it. Sometimes, these pierced the unmineralised strata and entered the next bed of limestone either above or below. For example, the name Underset Sump is a common one which indicates that an attempt to work or prove the vein in that strata had been made, usually from a level in the Main Limestone.

In Swaledale, miners in the stopes were paid by the amount of dressed ore they produced. They were paid at a rate of so much per bing, which was eight hundredweights, and the system was called bingtale. The rate paid depended on the ease with which the ore could be cut. If the vein was rich, therefore, they would be paid less than for working a poor vein. The miners driving levels, rises, sumps etc in the rock were paid on fathomtale, which was so much per fathom of advance. A few jobs, usually repairs or assisting other specialists, were paid on an hourly rate, called daytale.

These systems, whereby they were paid by results and largely supervised themselves, gave lead miners' a great deal of autonomy. They tended to work six hour shifts, but could work more, if they wanted to maximise a rich find, or less, if conditions were bad. As the 19th century passed, however, mine owners came to have more capital tied up in their mines and demanded longer hours from the men. Unlike coal miners, for whom shifts of 10 or more hours were common, lead miners were generally only expected to put in eight hours. In some instances, for example in Arkengarthdale, the men met this threat to their historic freedom by striking.

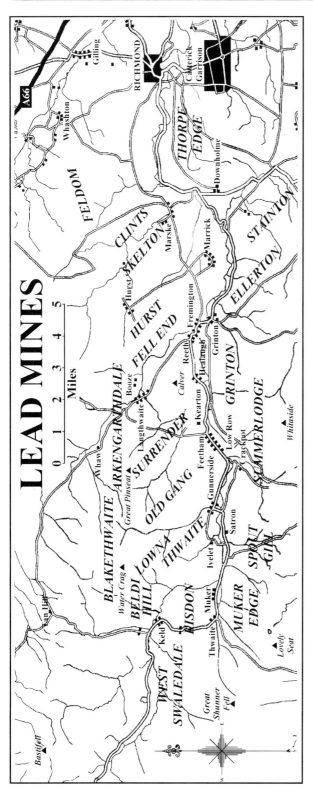

Principal Lead Mines in Swaledale and Arkengarthdale

DRESSING THE ORE

When it left the mine, the ore was mixed with rock, clay and other vein minerals and needed dressing to prepare it for smelting. All the techniques used by Dales' lead miners relied on the tendency for similar sized particles to separate according to their relative-density when agitated in water. The heaviest, i.e. lead ore at 7.6, went to the bottom, with progressively lighter material on top. The following is a simplified version of complex processes and the reader must remember that some dressing floors were much more mechanised and/or complicated than others.[13]

Bouse teams at Victoria Level

The run-of-mine ore, called bouse, was tipped into stone storage bays, called bouse-teams, which often had a small stream of water running through them to help loosen clay and gravel. On leaving the bouse-team, the water ran onto a grating of bars spaced one inch apart. The bouse was also raked onto this grate. Any bouse falling through the grate was called cuttings and it collected in a pit underneath. The oversize material was separated by hand, on a small table, to give the following three products: pure ore, which went to the bingstead; mixed ore and rock,

Waterwheel-powered roller crusher

Crushing rollers

Stone counter-weights

Wheel-ease

called chats; and worthless rock, which went to the waste heap.

The pieces of mixed ore and rock were crushed with either flat-faced hammers, called buckers, or with waterwheel-powered roller

Any pieces too large to go into the crusher were first broken to the size of a hen's egg using sledge hammers. In order to prevent hard stones etc. jamming them, the rollers were fitted with counter-weights which kept

Man using a hotching tub

crushers. Buckering was labour intensive and was done on stone anvils, called knockstones.

From around 1800 onwards, larger mines began using roller crushers which could crush around 10 tons per hour and took much less labour to run them.[14] This important saving meant that veins which had previously been too poor to work could be mined and dressed profitably. The waterwheels were typically 25 feet in diameter by three or four feet wide and, by gearing from the axle, drove two pairs of 14 inch diameter by 14 inch long rollers. These rollers turned in opposite directions and ore was fed onto them from a hopper.

them about 3/8ths of an inch apart, but allowed them to open up if a hard stone was encountered. The particle size produced by roller crushers was described as varying *"from that of a big pea to that of a big broad bean"*.

The crushed mineral was then treated in a hotching tub. This was a rectangular box, with a 3/8ths inch wire mesh bottom, which was suspended in a tub of water. The box hung from two forked straps on a long pivoted handle. The mineral was put on the sieve and then a boy jigged the long handle up and down causing the water to agitate it. Eventually, the fine (<3/8ths inch) material,

A Buddle

called smitham or smiddum, had gone through the sieve into the tub. The remainder had been sorted into three categories. The heavy pieces of clean ore had collected in a layer on the sieve, pieces of mixed ore and rock (chats) were in the middle and waste rock was on the top. These layers were carefully skimmed off, with the ore going to the bingstead, the waste rock to the dead heap and the chats being crushed smaller.

When the hotching tub became full of smitham, it was dug out and treated in a running buddle. This had a floor of flagstones or planks, which sloped down slightly from the back to the front, and had low walls on the back and sides. The back one had an opening to allow a steady stream of water in. The washer put a pile of smitham at the head of the buddle and used a rabble to rake it backwards, against the flow, thus keeping the purest and heaviest material there whilst allowing the lighter stuff to accumulate at the foot of the buddle. The very lightest particles were washed out of the buddle and carried to the slime pits, where they eventually settled out. The stuff from the buddle head was clean ore and it was taken to the bingstead. The smitham tails at the buddle foot held a considerable amount of ore, but were mixed with stony matter and clay. They were treated in a trunk buddle which had a compartment at its head into which a strong current of water flowed. The tails were piled at the head and stirred with a shovel. The biggest pieces of ore and stone were deposited at the head and were put to one side to be treated very

gently in a special hotching tub. The fines, however, were washed down the buddle and collected in its lower part. Those with the most ore were nearest the head, and those with the least were at the buddle foot. This deposit was split into three and each part was carefully washed again in the trunk buddle. This process was repeated until the product (slime ore) was pure enough for treatment in a dolly tub.

The latter was like a common washing tub, hence its name. It was filled with water and a paddle, or dolly, was put into it and rotated rapidly. Slime ore was added until enough of it was thoroughly mixed in. The dolly was then removed and workmen hit the tub sides with hammers to encourage the heavier particles to settle. The lightest ones only settled when the hammering stopped. The water was drained off and this upper part was thrown away. The pure ore at the bottom of the tub was taken to the bingstead. This device could also separate zinc blende which sometimes contaminated the lead ore.

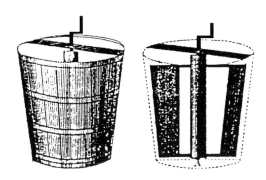

SMELTING THE ORE

In northern England most mines, or groups of mines, had their own smelting mill, whereas in Derbyshire and Wales the ore was sold to smelting companies.

Before mined ore (usually lead sulphide, PbS) could be smelted, it had to be dressed in order to separate it from any rock and vein minerals. The resulting concentrate was taken for smelting. This was done in two basic steps, although other processes (for example, roasting the concentrate to drive off moisture and some sulphur) were sometimes used. The first smelting took place between approximately 600° and 800° Celsius. It recovered from 40 to 75% of the metal and left a lead rich "grey slag". This went to the second stage which took place between 1000° and 1200° and melted the slags and any lead left in them.

The first step was done in an atmosphere which had an excess of oxygen and was, therefore, oxidising. Since the mediæval period, three principal methods have been used for this. These are bales (or boles), ore-hearths, and reverberatory furnaces and they are described below.

All methods of lead smelting relied on what is called a roast-reduction process. This is a complex series of reactions which produces, for example, lead oxide, -sulphate and -oxy-sulphate (= roasting or oxidation). These, probably as a liquid phase, react with each other and with remaining sulphide, to give lead and sulphur dioxide by double-decomposition (= reduction). It must be stressed, therefore, that these reactions are not between solids, but between liquids or gases and solids. The following chemical equations express in very simplified terms some of the reactions:-

$$2PbS + 3O_2 = 2PbO + 2SO_2$$
(roasting of lead sulphide in air and formation of lead oxide and sulphur dioxide)

$$2PbO + PbS = 3Pb + SO_2$$
(double-decomposition to lead and sulphur dioxide)

$$2PbS + 4O_2 = 2PbSO_4$$
(roasting and formation of lead sulphate)

$$PbS + PbSO_4 = 2Pb + 2SO_2$$
(double-decomposition to lead and sulphur dioxide)

The second step took place in a slag-hearth. This could produce a reducing atmosphere (i.e. in which any oxygen combined with carbon to make carbon monoxide, CO, by burning coke or charcoal in a shaft), and was used to smelt grey slag, which contained, especially, lead oxide and sulphate, with remaining lead sulphide from the foregoing reactions. These were produced as follows:-

$$2PbO + CO = 2Pb + CO_2$$

and

$$PbSO_4 + 2CO = Pb + SO_2 + 2CO_2$$

whilst liquid oxide or sulphate could also react with solid carbon:-

$$2PbO + C = 2Pb + CO_2$$

This substantially oversimplifies the complexity, as conditions near the blast were oxidising, so that roast reaction processes could also take place.

The molten slag and metal were tapped off as liquids and were easily separated because the slag floated on the metal. The resulting slag was widely referred to as "black" slag, and is a more-or-less black glass. In all cases, some lead was lost through volatilisation, but a proportion of this was recovered wherever mills used flues. Some lead also stayed in the black slags which were often further processed. The molten lead from both steps was cast into ingots, or pieces, of varying weights.

BALES

These were wind-blown hearths, built on exposed hillsides, often facing south-west, used for smelting lead in mediæval times. They are found throughout the Pennines, where their presence is often remembered in

A bellows blown bule

place-names. There is, however, an interesting and as yet unexplained difference between Derbyshire, where they are called Boles, and the north, where they are always called Bale or a variant of it (Bail, Bayle, Baal etc). Lawrence Barker, who has recorded over 50 of the area's bales, reported a radiocarbon date of AD 1464 +/- 25 years for charcoal from one on Calver, at Healaugh. Bales were widely used until the 1570s, when they were quickly replaced by smelt mills with ore-hearths.

Bales were between three and six feet in diameter, surrounded by a low stone wall and lined with clay. In this were placed alternating layers of firewood and ore. When lit, the fire burnt at relatively low temperatures (600 to 800° C) and pulled in air which helped to burn off the sulphur. As the fire progressed towards being a more compact mass of glowing embers, the chemical conditions changed and allowed the formation of molten lead. The latter collected in the bottom of the fire and was channelled into a hollow, where it set into a block or slab of lead.

THE ORE-HEARTH

In the 1570s an improved method of smelting, called the ore-hearth, spread from the Mendip area and quickly superseded the bale. The ore-hearth was a small, bellows-blown hearth in which the fuel (coal, wood or peat) was mixed with the concentrate. They were more economical to run than bales because they burnt billets of kiln-dried chopwood and could also smelt smaller pieces of ore. During the 18th century, however, smelters increasingly supplemented dried peat for wood as fuel, and sometimes added a proportion of coal. The peat was cut on local moors and stored in peat houses, where it dried. Remains of these can still be seen at some Swaledale mills (e.g. Grinton, Old Gang and Surrender).

The use of waterwheel-powered bellows meant that smelting no longer relied on the wind and could be done under much more controlled conditions in what became known as smelt mills. A few early smelt mills are recorded elsewhere, but none are known in Swaledale until 1575, when one was built at

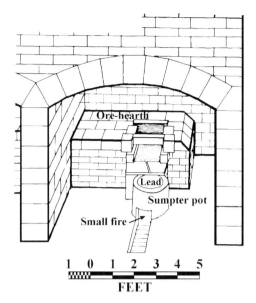

Ore-hearth

(Lead)

Sumpter pot

Small fire

1 0 1 2 3 4 5

FEET

Marrick, and 1589, when another was built at Clints, in Marske. Because the bale smelters had already used much of the woodland in the upper dale, these early mills were built further down the valley, where there were more trees to supply the timber needed for fuel. Altogether, there have been 36 lead mills in Swaledale and Arkengarthdale, plus eight more in Wensleydale, and three copper mills at Middleton Tyas. A few early mills may remain unrecognised on the eastern fringe of the lead mining area where, for example, the base of an ore-hearth was found at Downholme, where no mill is known.

The ore-hearth, which remained unchanged for the next 350 years and was used at most Yorkshire smelt mills, had the advantage of being both cheap and easy to build. Unlike reverberatory furnaces, which performed best if worked continuously, ore-hearths were well suited to dealing with interrupted periods of smelting, which were common on smaller mines. Even in its later, much improved, forms, the ore-hearth was never very large, its interior being in the region of two feet wide by 18 inches high by 12 inches deep. It stood inside a stone-arched canopy, which gave space for the smelters to work and led any fumes into the chimney. Despite being called stones, the parts of an

ore-hearth were usually made from iron by the early 18th century as this greatly extended their life. These stones were the pan bottom; work stone; bearer (2); key stone (4); pipe stone; back stone and fore stone. They were enclosed by fire bricks and any unwanted voids were packed with sand or clay. Because they were easily broken up for scrap, no ore-hearths have survived, but the remains of the arches can often be identified and some survive intact.

The work stone, which both projected and sloped forward from the top, front edge of the pan bottom, was about two feet square. It was crossed by a groove, called a riggot, which took the molten lead from the hearth into a heated container called a sumpter pot. At the rear of the hearth, the pipe stone sat on the pan bottom and had a notch in its top edge to carry the tuyère, or bellows nozzle. The back stone sat on top of the pipe stone. The two bearers, which were about four inches square and about two feet long, sat on

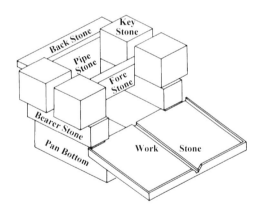

Key Stone

Back Stone

Pipe Stone

Fore Stone

Bearer Stone

Pan Bottom

Work Stone

Parts of the Ore-Hearth

either side of the pan bottom and formed the sides of the hearth. This formed a reservoir for molten lead which helped maintain the hearth's temperature and reduce corrosion. The four key stones, which were cubes of about ten inch sides, sat on the bearers, two either side, and held the fore stone in place.

The cold hearth was filled with peat bricks, which were about twelve inches long by three inches wide and three inches thick. The bricks

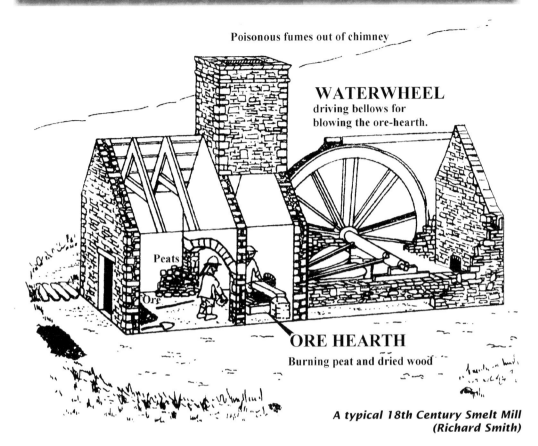

Poisonous fumes out of chimney

WATERWHEEL
driving bellows for
blowing the ore-hearth.

Peats

Ore

ORE HEARTH
Burning peat and dried wood

A typical 18th Century Smelt Mill
(Richard Smith)

at the front were built into a wall and the others were tossed in behind them. A burning brick of peat was then put in front of the tuyère, the wind from which quickly spread the fire. A few shovelfuls of coal were thrown on top of the peat to increase the heat, and to make the fire last longer and burn steadily.

When the fuel was well alight, some browse, which was partly smelted mineral from an earlier smelting, was thrown on. After this (and sometimes before all the browse had been thrown onto the fire), the greater part of the hearth's contents was pulled onto the workstone with a large iron rake, called a gavelock. The mineral waste, called grey slag, which an experienced smelter distinguished by its being brighter than the browse, was shovelled to one side of the hearth. The browse left on the workstone was put back into the hearth and a little coal added if necessary. Lime was sometimes also added to

help the browse separate from the slag, by causing clayey, siliceous and ferruginous substances to reunite into lumps. The lime also helped to release lead trapped in refractory substances.

A half brick of peat was next put in front of the tuyère in order to diffuse the air throughout the fire and several shovelfuls of concentrates were spread on top. The hearth was then left for between 10 and 15 minutes before its contents were again pulled onto the workstone and the grey slag removed. A new peat was put in front of the tuyère and coal and lime were added before the browse was thrown back into the hearth and more concentrate put on top. This work, repeated 14 or 15 times, formed a smelting shift, during which time from two to four tons of lead were made. At the end of a shift, any remaining browse was put aside to begin the next smelting.

FUMES AND FLUES

On leaving the furnace, the hot gases carried a mixture of fine particles of lead oxides and sulphate, called fume, plus copious amounts of sulphur dioxide. Early smelt mills had short, vertical chimneys directly over the furnaces until after 1778, when a horizontal flue was built to prevent lead fume from the Middleton Dale Upper Cupola, in Derbyshire, from poisoning nearby pastures. Animals are said to have found that grass on which lead fume had settled tasted sweet, but they soon died. The flue at Middleton Dale led to a remote chimney on the side of a hill, allowing the gases to slow down and cool, thereby depositing the lead fume in the flue. The discovery of its value as means of recovering fume, however, appears to have been purely providential. Even as late as the 1830s, most flues were seldom over 100 yards long and it was not until the 1840s that many of the long flues were built. Nevertheless, the flue at the Octagon Mill, in Arkengarthdale, was 915 yards long by 1821. Like soot in any chimney, the fume coated the walls of the flue and men were sent in to brush it off. Even with the furnaces cold, work in such conditions was hazardous, but the longevity of many smelters suggests that tales of lead poisoning leading to death were the stuff of late-Victorian or Edwardian melodrama.

By the 1840s experiments were also being made to condense even more of the lead fume by forcing it through filters and sprays of water. Every so often, the deposits of lead soot were swept from the flue walls and washed into settlement pits near the smelt mill. When dry, the fume was smelted in the slag-hearth and lead recovered from it.

THE SLAG HEARTH

This was used both for smelting slags from other processes and for some poor quality ores. It was a shaft furnace, around 26 inches long by 22 inches wide and 33 inches high. The furnace bottom was a two-inch-thick slab of cast-iron sole plate, which sloped slightly from back to front. Sitting on either side of this were two bearers, similar to those in an ore-hearth, which supported the two iron forestones. The latter, which stand vertically one above the other, were each 12 inches high by 26 inches long. They were separated by a single course of fire-bricks, two inches high. There was a gap of about seven inches between the lowest of these plates and the sole. The back of the hearth, from the sole up to the tuyère, was made from a single iron plate about 20 inches high. The sides, above the bearers, and the back, above the tuyère, were built from open-grained free-stone.

The bottom of the hearth was filled, to within two or three inches of the tuyère, with partly burnt and well compacted coke. This acted as a filter for the molten lead and slag. In front of the hearth was a split sumpter pot with its first part also filled with the compacted, partly burnt coke. The molten lead sank through this and emerged in the other half of the sumpter pot, but the molten slag ran over it into a bath of cold water. The chilling effect of the water shattered the slags, making it easier to recover any small pieces of lead they contained.

At the start of a smelting shift, the bottom part of the hearth was filled with bricks of peat and a burning one placed before the tuyère. This quickly spread the flame to the other peats and then a layer of coke was shovelled on top. Once the coke was well alight, a layer of grey-slag was spread on top of it. From time to time, coke and slag were thrown on in alternate layers. The burning coke produced a reducing atmosphere (i.e. one in which oxygen combined with carbon to form carbon monoxide, CO) and reacted with the lead oxide and sulphate and any remaining lead sulphide as follows:-

$$PbO + CO = 2Pb + CO_2$$

and

$$PbSO_4 + 2CO = Pb + SO_2 + 2CO_2$$

whilst liquid oxide or sulphate could also react with solid carbon

$$2PbO + C = 2Pb + CO_2$$

This substantially oversimplifies the complexity, as conditions near the blast were oxidising, so that roast reaction processes could also take place.

Two workmen, sometimes a man and a boy, worked the slag-hearth. The shift varied in length from 14 to 16 hours and from one to two tons of lead were made. This lead was harder than ore-hearth lead, because it contained impurities, and so was sold at a slightly lower price. In later years, some big smelt mills, like that the Old Gang, installed softening furnaces to improve the value of their lead.

REVERBERATORY OR CUPOLA FURNACES

Another form of lead smelting was the reverberatory or cupola furnace, which appears to have been developed for copper smelting in the Bristol area around 1670. This furnace burnt raw coal in a separate fire-box, the heat (but not the fumes) from which was reflected (or reverberated) on to the concentrate. This type of furnace ran somewhat hotter than the others and must have reached 1100° to 1200° because it also melted the slag. The molten slag, in the cupola, floated on the metal and was either tapped off as a liquid or mixed with lime to solidify it before being drawn out of the furnace with a rake. This slag was then taken to the slag-hearth.

Such furnaces were widely used in Derbyshire and North Wales, but were rare in Yorkshire, being used at only five or six mills, only two of which were in Swaledale.

THE MINERAL LORDS

The surface and the minerals (except gold and silver) under it would once have had common owners, but the rights to them have often been divorced through the sale of one and retention of the other. The mineral lord was the person, or persons, who owned the minerals, and from whom permission to mine them was sought.

Some lords took an active part in mining, but others did not, preferring instead to receive an income from rents and a duty, or royalty, on all the lead produced. This duty was an agreed proportion of the lead, often 1/5th in the 18th century, which was handed over to the mineral lord free of all charges. In Swaledale, the mineral lords' agents then sold it to lead merchants at Stockton or Hull.

Fortunately, the boundaries of the mineral properties, or liberties, usually agreed fairly well with those of the civil parishes, but accurate boundaries were very important and major disputes, often accompanied by violence, sometimes broke out where a boundary crossed featureless moorland. The disputed land may only have amounted to a few tens of yards either way, but this could account for thousands of pounds from any veins which crossed them and legal cases arising from such disputes are a rich source of information on the mines.

In the description of the mining areas which follows, the part played by the respective mineral lords is discussed in the relevant section. Much of upper Swaledale, including the parishes of Reeth, Melbecks and Muker were, however, owned by the Lords Wharton, and their descendants. So, to avoid repetition and because the history of

ownership is complicated, a description of it now follows.

In return for his support, Henry VIII granted Sir Thomas Wharton the manor of Muker and a half share of the adjoining manor of Healaugh in 1544. Philip, Fourth Lord Wharton paid £3173 for the other half of Healaugh in 1635, and thereby gained rights over minerals in much of Swaledale west of Reeth. The first evidence of the family's direct involvement in mining came in February 1668, when this Philip Wharton leased his mines in Healaugh to Philip Swale and Robert Barker.

The fifth Lord's son and heir, another Philip, was created the first Duke of Wharton in January 1718, but he was an unstable spendthrift and, in addition to spending the family fortune, he espoused the cause of the Young Pretender in the attack on Gibraltar by the Spaniards. For this act of treason he lost his estates in 1729.

This Philip died in 1731, and in April 1733 the Court of Chancery placed his estates in the hands of trustees for the payment of his debts. The residue was to be shared equally between his only sisters, Lady Jane Coke and Lady Lucy Morice. The Trust's principal mines were those now regarded as the Old Gang, but this name is never used in the accounts, which always describe them as *'the Lead Mines in Swaledale in the possession of the Trustees of the late Duke of Wharton'*. The mines were in three groups, at Swinnergill, Lownathwaite and Merryfield.

Thomas Smith, of Gray's Inn London, bought the manors of Healaugh and Muker from the Trustees for £10,500 in 1738. The sale reserved mines of lead, copper and iron ore in all the common and waste lands for the use of the Trustees, and Smith got the rights to the coal mines, including the Tanhill Colliery, which lay in the wastes. This meant that Smith, as the manorial lord, had nothing to do with lead mining on the unenclosed moors, but the ambiguous wording of the agreement led to disputes which were not settled until the 1770s. Sometimes relations between the Lords of the Manor and the mine lessors became very acrimonious. For example, Thomas Smith was not slow to protect his newly acquired property and brought court actions which confirmed his rights over mines in the enclosed lands. This included mines at Fryer Intake, the lower part of Gunnerside Gill and at Beldi Hill.

Smith and his successors as Lords of the Manor were:-

Thomas Smith (1)	1738 - 1773
Thomas Smith (2)	1773 - 1817
Rev. Thomas Smith	1817 - 1868
Eleanor Sillery	1868 - 1879
Francis Horner Lyell	1879 - 1934

The mineral rights, meanwhile, passed down as follows. When Lady Lucy Morice died without issue in 1739, her moiety returned to Lady Jane Coke. She died in 1761 and left her estate to Anna-Maria Draycott, formerly Delagard, of Sunbury, Middlesex.

After the trust was wound up, the mineral rights passed to Anna-Maria Draycott, who married George Fermor, the 2nd Earl of Pomfret, on April 30th 1764. Thus, the manorial ownership between 1544 and 1738, and then the mineral ownership to 1764, was as follows:-

Thomas Wharton (1st Lord)	1544-1568
Thomas Wharton (2nd Lord)	1568-1572
Philip Wharton (3rd Lord)	1572-1629
Philip Wharton (4th Lord)	1629-1696
Thomas Wharton (5th Lord)	1696-1715
Philip Duke of Wharton	1715-1731
Duke of Wharton's Trustees	1733-1764
George Fermor + Anna-Maria Draycott	
	1764-1787

When the 2nd Earl of Pomfret died in 1785, he was succeeded by his eldest son, also called George Fermor, as the 3rd Earl. This George and his younger brother, Thomas William Fermor, each inherited a quarter share in the minerals, while their sister, Lady Charlotte, who married Peter Denys in 1787, got a half share.

Peter Denys managed the Earl's Yorkshire estates and, because there was no suitable place to stay near the mines, they jointly purchased a house belonging to Thomas Elliot in Low Fremington in 1792. Peter Denys enlarged the house, laid out the gardens and named it AD Hall, after the mines.

During the 19th century, these joint mineral lords were generally known as either the AD Lessors or the AD Proprietors. Their policy, from the 1780s onwards, was to split the mines into blocks and lease them to groups of venture capitalists. Nevertheless, the lessors sometimes also held shares in the mines, and one, Sir G. W. Denys (2nd Bt), was an active partner in a series of ventures.

This propensity to name everything AD is sometimes a source of confusion, and a brief explanation is necessary. There are two possible origins of the title AD. The first relates to the initials of Anna-Maria Draycott, but this is unlikely because the AD mark was being stamped on pieces of lead produced by the smelting mills by 1750, when she was only fourteen. It is much more likely, therefore, that they are the initials of Alexander Denton, the head of the Duke of Wharton's trustees. The AD Lessors had a share in the company working the Surrender mine from 1792, and were comprised of William Chaytor and his son, John Breare, and the lessors (Pomfret and Denys) who had a quarter share. Pomfret and Denys' mills are called the AD mills throughout the accounts, and from 1873 to 1887 there was also the AD Lead Mining Company Ltd, in which Sir George Denys (2nd Bt) had a share. (The Arkindale and Derwent Company is also sometimes called AD, but had no connection with the Swaledale mines. Instead, this worked in Arkengarthdale from 1812 to 1817.)

Lord Pomfret's son-in-law, Peter Denys, was an ambitious man and purchased a pavilion at Chelsea as well as AD Hall. Lord Pomfret used his influence with George IV to get Peter a peerage, which the King refused, offering a Baronetcy instead. Peter refused, but accepted on behalf of his eldest son George, who was created a baronet in 1813, at the age of twenty three.

Like the Duke of Wharton, however, Sir George indulged himself in every extravagance and he soon had to go abroad to avoid his creditors. So, when Peter Denys died, in 1816, he left all his estate to his wife, to teach his reckless son a lesson. In the same year, however, the 3rd Earl of Pomfret gave Sir George Denys his quarter share in the minerals.

When Lady Charlotte died in 1835, a quarter share of the minerals, the pavilion in Chelsea, the AD Hall and £80,000 were left to her daughter, Anna-Maria, who had married Sir Francis Shuckburgh in 1825. They first moved the pavilion's contents to Shuckburgh and then sold it around 1852. It was pulled down in 1883. Sir George W. Denys (1st Bt) also got a quarter share of the minerals, giving him a half in total. When he died in 1857, this share and his title passed to his son, who was also called George and became the second baronet. The latter died in February 1881 and was followed by his son Francis, who changed his name to Sir Francis Denys-Burton in the summer of 1906.

The 3rd Earl of Pomfret was married, but died without issue in 1830 and so was succeeded by his brother Thomas, who had the remaining quarter share. He had four children, but, when he died in 1833, his share passed to his wife, Amabel Elizabeth, Countess of Pomfret. She died in 1889, but some time earlier had split the share equally between her two daughters (Anna Maria Annabella and Henrietta Louisa) and their successors. The first daughter's 1/8th share passed to her son, Sir Thomas George Fermor-Hesketh, while the second daughter's widower sold her 1/8th share to Sir Francis Denys soon after she died. Around 1889, therefore, Sir Francis Denys had 5/8ths of the minerals, Sir Stewkley F.D. Shuckburgh had 1/4th and Sir Thomas George Fermor-Hesketh had 1/8th.

For completeness, the following is a list of the mineral lords' agents:-

	FROM	TO
Jeremiah Hutchinson	1765	1767
John Metcalfe	1767	1774
William Brown	1774	1777
Francis Gill	1796	1801
John Davies	1802	1822
James Littlefair	1824	1861
Ralph Place	1861	1872
Thomas Raw	1873	1883
Simon Cherry	1884	1901
Edward Cherry	1901	1928

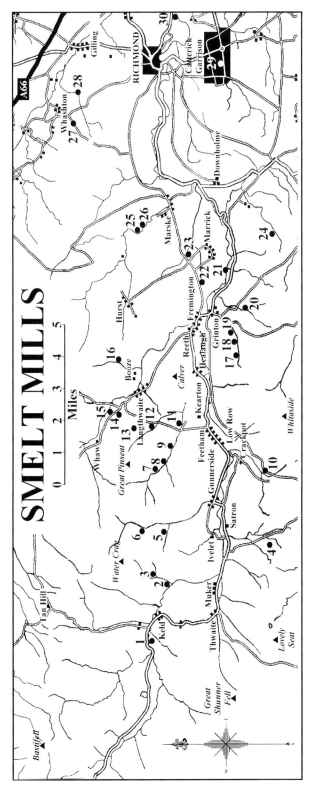

SMELT MILLS

Miles

0 1 2 3 4 5

Smelt mill in Swaledale and Arkenguithdale

LIST OF SWALEDALE SMELT MILLS

SITE	NAME	WORKING LIFE FROM	TO	GRID REF
1	Keldside	1835	1862	NY879016
2	Beldi Hill	1770	1883	NY909005
3	Swinnergill	1807	1819	NY912012
4	Spout Gill	1735	c1770	SD931956
5	Lownathwaite	1769	1823	NY935006
6	Blakethwaite	1821	1878	NY937018
7	New	1797	1846	NY975005
	Old Gang	1846	1901	NY975005
8	High or Ray Gill	1674 or 82	1805	NY978003
9	Smith's	1769	1772	NY982002
10	Summerlodge	1810	c1857	SD966950
11	Low (at Surrender)	1674 or 82	1840	NY991999
	New (at Surrender)	1685	1840	NY991999
	Surrender	1841	1880	NY991999
12	Low Moulds	pre 1719	1804	NY992010
13	High Moulds	1785	1804	NY989019
14	CB Mill	1822-23	1903	NY996034
15	Octagon Mill	1804	1821	NY996036
16	Farndale	pre 1718	?	NZ019028
17	Grovebeck	c1761	c1769?	SE028970
18	New	c1770	c1825?	SE034971
19	Scott's	c1769	1868	SE038973
20	Grinton How	c1728	1893	SE049964
21	Ellerton	pre 1682	post 1768	SE069976
22	Cupola	1701	pre 1725	SE063987
23	Sayer's or Low	1574-75	pre 1700	SE078994
	Marrick High	pre 1660	c1838	SE079994
	Marrick Low	c1838	1874	SE078994
24	Stainton	1786	1820s?	SE090952
25	Phillip's	c1583	c1605	NZ089021
26	Willance's	c1605	c1767	NZ092175
	Bathurst's	c1700	c1767	NZ092175
27	Whashton	pre 1671	c1725	NZ144055
28	Gilling	c1630?	c1700	NZ159057
29	Waitwith	pre 1671	c1675	SE171976
30	Easby	late C17th?	early C18th	NZ196003

South Swaledale

This group of small mines, on the south side of the valley between Muker and Thwaite, worked veins which cross the watershed from Wensleydale. From around 1730, a company of national importance leased the lead mines between Spout Gill, Keldside and Sleddale from the Trustees of the Duke of Wharton. This was the Company of Mine Adventurers of England, which was a joint stock company, established in 1698, with extensive mining interests in Cardiganshire and Montgomeryshire. The company had its own smelt mill at Spout Gill, a drawing of which has survived.

When the company gave up its lease around 1757, Thomas Smith claimed that Spout Gill mill was part of the Lordship of the manor of Healaugh, which he had purchased in 1738. Under this pretext, the lessees of Smith's mines at Beldi Hill smelted their ore at Spout Gill until June 1769 when Lord Pomfret's agents took forcible possession of the mill. The mill then stood idle until January 1835, when Richard Carter began working the old slags and eventually made 1.37 tons of lead.

STOCKDALE

In 1841, Thomas Hunter & company produced 4.3 tons of lead from a major east to west fault, which runs through Stockdale. The vein, which in Stockdale has been tried from two hushes and a level, runs down Swaledale, but has only carried significant mineralisation on Ellerton Moor, where it is called Great Stork Vein.

LOVER GILL

This mine, which was also called Glover Gill Mine, was worked by Thomas, Lord Wharton in 1715, and the Company of Mine Adventurers of England produced 37 tons of ore there between 1751 and 1755. It is on the northern continuation of Staggs Fell Vein, which was being worked by the London Lead Company at the same time. The Mine Adventurers probably began Lover Gill Hush, where the vein has the 4th (Five Yard) Limestone on the north-west, or downthrow, side.

The vein has also been worked by opencasting and shallow shafts in the Main Limestone opposite the Butter Tubs. Kearton's Level, which had been driven to the vein in the Underset Limestone by 1843, was reopened by the South Swaledale Lead Mining Company Ltd in 1868, but was abandoned in May 1871.

MUKER EDGE OR PROVIDENCE MINE

The vein which outcrops in the Main Limestone on Muker Edge is the one worked by Sargill Mine, in Wensleydale. Ralph Milner and company leased the mine for 14 years from 1828, paying 1/6th duty. Their lease was renewed, however, and they worked until 1861, raising enough ore between 1828 and 1847 to make 260 tons of lead. They drove a High and a Low Level into the Main Limestone and found flots alongside the vein.

David Harker, who was working for the

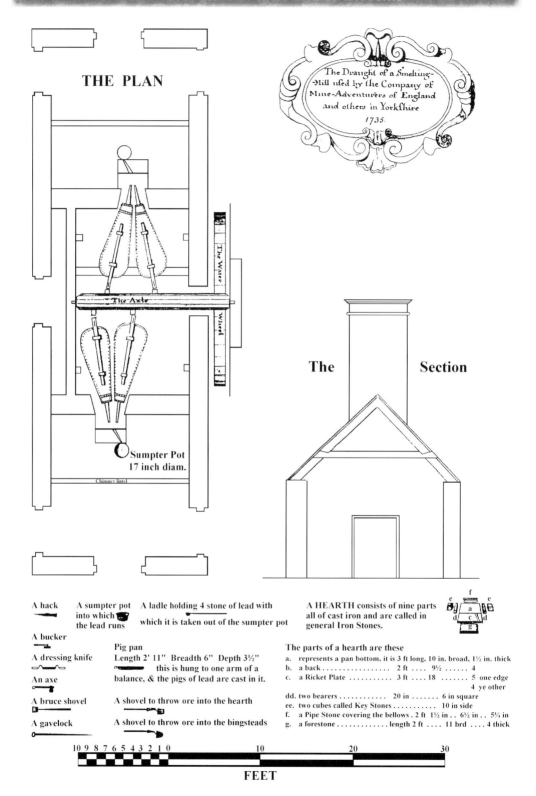

THE PLAN

The Draught of a Smelting-
-Mill used by the Company of
Mine-Adventurers of England
and others in Yorkshire
1735.

The Water Wheel

The Axle

Sumpter Pot
17 inch diam.

Chimney lintel

The   Section

A hack

A bucker

A dressing knife

An axe

A bruce shovel

A gavelock

A sumpter pot
into which
the lead runs

A ladle holding 4 stone of lead with

which it is taken out of the sumpter pot

Pig pan
Length 2' 11" Breadth 6" Depth 3½"
this is hung to one arm of a
balance, & the pigs of lead are cast in it.

A shovel to throw ore into the hearth

A shovel to throw ore into the bingsteads

A HEARTH consists of nine parts
all of cast iron and are called in
general Iron Stones.

The parts of a hearth are these
a.   represents a pan bottom, it is 3 ft long, 10 in. broad, 1½ in. thick
b.   a back . . . . 2 ft 9½ 4
c.   a Ricket Plate . . . . 3 ft . . . . 18 . . . . 5 one edge
                                                                    4 ye other
dd. two bearers . . . . 20 in . . . . 6 in square
ee. two cubes called Key Stones . . . . 10 in side
f.   a Pipe Stone covering the bellows . 2 ft 1½ in . . 6½ in . . 5¾ in
g.   a forestone . . . . length 2 ft . . . . 11 brd . . . . 4 thick

10 9 8 7 6 5 4 3 2 1 0   10   20   30

FEET

South Swaledale Lead Mining Company Ltd, found encouraging signs of ore in December 1864 and so the company began a new level to try the vein in the Underset Limestone. Like most of the veins on the south side of Swaledale, the best ore was in flots, but these were of limited extent and soon worked out. Nevertheless, between 1867 and 1871 the mine produced some 380 tons of lead.

The mine closed in 1871, but a note from Thomas Raw, the AD Lessor's agent, shows that it was briefly reopened in 1881, when some ore was found in Modesty flot.

SPOUT GILL AND SATRON MINES

Many of the veins worked by this group of mines, from Spout Gill east to the boundary with Grinton, also cross the watershed from Wensleydale. Here, too, much of the ore came from flots. As already noted, the Company of Mine Adventurers of England had its smelt mill at Spout Gill, on a tributary stream called Foss Gill. It also worked some of the veins here.

Oxnop Vein can be seen running northwards, alongside the road from Askrigg to Satron as it enters the head of Oxnop Gill. To the east of it three strings, which run north from Beezy Mine, were worked from shallow shafts into the Main Limestone at Simon Grooves during the 18th century. The area was prospected by the South Swaledale Lead Mining Company Ltd which, in 1865, employed Bernard Calvert & Sons to drive a level in search of a flot on Beezy Old Vein. Interest in the area continued and in June 1916, George Calvert was credited with raising 10 cwts of ore from Oxnop Gill Mine.

In June 1918, Pickup and Fawcett applied for, and were granted, a two year take note to work Satron Moor and Spoutgill Mines. They employed six men and tried Oxnop Vein near Jenkin Gate, where they found some lumps of ore, and drove a level at Stottergill, but abandoned both places as being unviable. They then turned their attention to Arngill, across the valley.

At their northern ends, the veins at Simon Grooves are cut off by Stottergill Vein, an extension of Summerlodge Vein in Grinton, which in turn is called Brownfield Vein in Wensleydale. Stottergill Vein had been worked in the 18th century, but in 1823 it was leased to William Metcalfe and company, who raised two-and-a-half tons between 1824 and 1826. Metcalfe's lease was for 15 years, but no more work appears to have been done.

Spout Gill Vein, which is nearly parallel to Stottergill Vein, but about 2000 feet north of it, was leased to Edward Thompson, Alderman of York, in November 1682. The trial came to nothing, however, and in the following September Philip Swale complained to Lord Wharton that the miners at Oxnop Gill had been allowed to walk away. Thomas, Lord Wharton's miners tried the vein in 1715, and the Company of Mine Adventurers of England got 200 tons of lead there between 1750 and 1756. The vein was worked intermittently throughout the rest of the 18th century, but the next sustained production came between 1819 and 1827, when James Brown produced 100 tons of lead.

Satron Walls East and West Veins run northwards and outcrop in crags formed by the Main Limestone, at Satron High and Low Walls. Thomas Calvert produced 18 tons of lead from Satron Walls between 1819 and 1845, and Metcalfe & Company produced 27 tons of lead from Satron Moor between 1842 and 1849.

West Swaledale Mines

This group of three mines lies at the head of Swaledale, above Keld. Keldside, the first mine, and Lane End, the last, are 1¼ miles apart and belonged to the AD Lessors. Little Moor Foot, on the other hand, was in the old enclosures, owned by the Lord of the Manor. Our understanding of the mines is made difficult by the absence of sections showing the workings and their geology. Nevertheless, the beds dip gently westward and the valley bottom rises in the same direction, making the top of the Main Limestone, which is immediately below the river at Keldside Mine, around 350 feet deep

at Lane End Mine. This meant that the beds were flooded and, with the exception of a few short levels, none of the mines could be worked without pumping. This was expensive and, in order to be viable, they were generally worked as one during the 19th century.

LANE END MINE

What is thought to be Middle Vein outcropped in the bed of the river here, and the North Vein, which has an eight fathom throw, carried ore in the 10 Fathom Grit.

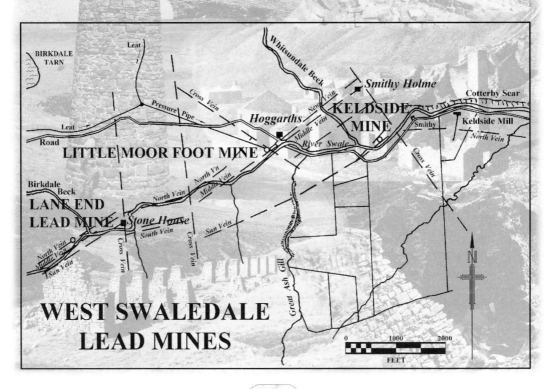

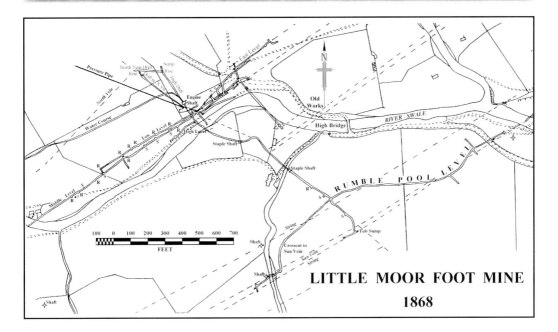

LITTLE MOOR FOOT MINE
1868

Thomas Butson & Company leased this mine for 21 years in 1801. They were to pay an annual rent of £20 and 1/6th duty, and to sink a new engine shaft and employ at least four men. Butson's, or New Engine Shaft was 50 fathoms deep and its name suggests that there was an earlier shaft here. It was pumped by a waterwheel, but by 1815 the wheel was not powerful enough to keep the mine dry and it closed.

Messrs Hopper, who already had Swinnergill Mine, worked the mine next and probably began driving Scott's Level. This starts in the 27 Fathom Grit, at the side of the river Swale about 1200 feet north-west of Keld, and would have drained the Main Limestone at Keldside. It was though to have been 200 fathoms long and heading west in North Vein when Hopper abandoned it around 1824.

Henry Jackson & Company leased all three mines in 1829 and installed an 80 H.P. engine, bought second-hand from Ashton Green Colliery. This was at a time of very low lead prices however, and, when a group of local mining agents inspected the mine in October 1830, they advised driving Scott's Level up to the shaft as soon as possible and abandoning the engine. The shaft had reached the top of the Main Chert at a depth of 50 fathoms, but the beds were so full of water that the agents advised against sinking any deeper. It is not clear what the company did, but it gave up the mines in 1839 and very little work appears to have been done there since. The 1857 OS map shows a waterwheel for pumping and a 'ventilation machine'.

LITTLE MOOR FOOT

Because this mine belonged to the Lord of the Manor, not the AD Lessors, no records of its output appear in the latter's accounts. It was worked from a 47 fathom deep shaft, which must begin in the 10 Fathom Grit because it is said to end in the top part of the plate above the Underset Lime. Middle Vein has a slight hade northwards and was worked from a branch of Rumble Pool Level, called High Level, and a Middle and Low Level, both from the shaft, which were probably in the Main Chert and Limestone. To the north of Middle Vein, North and New Veins were tried from crosscuts, as were some strings to the south, but very little work was done.

A firm of Newcastle lead merchants, Cookson & Company, ran the mines between 1841 and 1847, but, apart from their producing 180 tons of lead from Lane End and Keldside, we know nothing about their work. A leat, which runs to the mine from Birkdale Beck, suggests that the mine was pumped by a waterwheel during the 1830s and 1840s.

Christopher Lonsdale Bradley, who was also working at Blakethwaite, took the mines next and worked them as the West Swaledale Company. He put a hydraulic engine on Little Moor Foot Engine Shaft and supplied it with water from Birkdale Tarn. It lifted the water around 37 fathoms to Rumble Pool Level, and was also said to drain Butson's Shaft, at Lane End, presumably through the vein network.

KELDSIDE MINES

The Company of Mine Adventurers of England made the first significant attempt to work the veins here in the 1740s and got

and it is just as likely that they were what became Little Moor Foot and Keldside Mines respectively.

Tissington's company, which was also working for copper at Middleton Tyas, spent £688 13s 7d at High Birkdale between 1753 and 1758, but appears to have found little ore. The company also built what was described as an engine on a piece of land called Great Dales in 1756, when David Cleasby was paid a wayleave of 10s 0d for carrying *"wood etc through his land for the engine"*. This was almost certainly a horse whim, which was used to work pumps. This trial also failed and in the spring of 1760 the engine was taken down and the pumps taken from the shaft.

Messrs Hopper drove Rumble Pool Level to try the Keldside veins to the west of that mine. Richardson's Level, on the south side of the river at Keldside, was probably driven by Henry Jackson & Company, and most of the 200 tons of lead they produced from 1835 to 1838 came from Keldside. The Company of Mine Adventurers of England smelted Keldside ore at its Spout Gill Smelt Mill, but a covenant of Jackson's

Keldside smelt mill

88.28 tons of lead between 1751 and 1753, but gave up soon afterwards. They were followed by a company headed by George Tissington, and Thomas and Ralph Parkes, who had two mines, called High and Low Birkdale. Raistrick believed the latter to be Lane End, but this remains to be proved

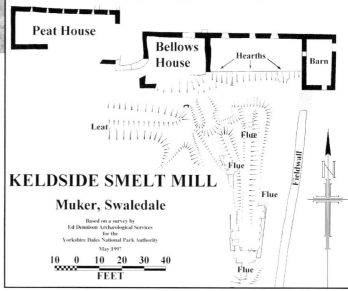

Peat House

Bellows House

Hearths

Barn

Leat

Flue

Flue

Flue

Fieldwall

Flue

Flue

KELDSIDE SMELT MILL

Muker, Swaledale

Based on a survey by
Ed Dennison Archaeological Services
for the
Yorkshire Dales National Park Authority

May 1997

10   0   10   20   30   40
FEET

N

Keldside smelt mill - detail of window

lease was that a mill would be built when there was enough ore to make six marks (31.4 tons) of lead. Because the industry was entering a massive slump, however, no lead was made until August 1835.

As we have seen, the mines closed at the *"end of 1861"*, but the mill would have smelted any stocks of ore before also closing soon afterwards. The buildings were maintained until November 1897, when the roofs were stripped and their slates and timber sold by auction.

Parts of the mill, which has been converted for agricultural use, are difficult to interpret, though it appears to have been split into three main parts. The eastern end was probably an office, while the central part was the smelting room, with two ore-hearths and a slag-hearth, and the western end was the bellows room, with a waterwheel on its southern side. Behind the mill, each hearth had its own flue, which united and led to a chimney some 540 feet behind the mill. A second building, about 50 feet long and at the mill's western end, was the peat house.

A piece of land between the smelt mill and the river is called *"Stamp Mill Green"* on an 1824 map, but no buildings are shown. It is likely, therefore, that this relates to crushing machinery used by the Company of Mine Adventurers of England.

By 1860 the Little Engine and Engine Shafts, on the north side of the river, were 12 and 18 fathoms deep respectively. They worked the North and Sun Strings in the Main Limestone and were pumped by a four foot breast by 20 foot diameter waterwheel, which also drove a crushing mill. An old Engine Shaft, on the south side of the river, worked a north to south cross vein and may have been where Messrs Hopper's miners reputedly worked below the river until it broke through and flooded them out, presumably around 1824.

Whilst we do not know how well the West Swaledale Company did at Little Moor Foot, it only produced 80 tons of lead from Keldside between 1851 and 1859. In March 1863, Robert Lowes, who had been the company's agent since 1843, reported that the mine had been closed since the end of 1861 and, whilst no one was underground, the engines were still running.

When it became clear that Bradley was not going to reopen the mines, Sir George Denys began planning a new company to work them. Bradley was in no rush to sell his plant to the new company, however, and the sale was not

Keldside smelt mill chimney

agreed until early May 1865. In June 1865 the prospectus of the Keld Side Lead Mining Company Limited was published in the *Mining Journal*. Its capital was to be £15,000, split into 750 shares of £20 each, and the public was informed that *"negotiations are also in progress for the leasing of Littlemoor Mine"* where *"extensive workings have formerly been carried on, and large quantities of ore have been raised"*! The public was not so easily impressed, however, and the company was under-subscribed and, in August, returned all the money that it had received.

Undeterred, a second company was being planned even as the first was being floated. This was the Lane End, Keldside and Littlemoor Lead Mining Company Limited. Its capital was to be £30,000, split into 6000 shares of £5 each. Lane End & Keld Side Mines were held on a 21 year lease, at 1/8th duty, and Little Moor Foot was held under lease from Mrs Sillery, as Lady of the Manor, for a term of 21 years at 1/10th duty. This company also came to nothing.

In readiness for the above schemes, the Kisdon Mining Company, of which Sir George Denys was a director, began driving the Sir George Level in 1864. This was intended to drain the Keld Side Veins, and it was hoped that enough ore to cover the cost of driving the level would be raised from the Middle Vein, but it proved to be barren. Faced with carrying the entire cost, the company stopped the level around April 1867, when it was 113 fathoms long. A few more fathoms were driven between October 1867 and May 1868, when the project was abandoned. The mouth of the level, which begins in the 27 Fathom Grit, below the Underset Limestone, has been buried by a landslip.

The same company also reopened Richardson's Level, near Keldside Smelt Mill, and drove a 12 fathom long crosscut in search of the South Vein, but did not find it. The level was abandoned in May 1868.

STONESDALE MOOR

Christopher Lonsdale Bradley followed Blakethwaite Vein westwards until it dipped below his lowest level. Faced with the cost of sinking deeper and the amount of water already entering the workings, he gave up Blakethwaite Mine on August 23rd 1861. In 1850, however, he also leased ground in

West Stonesdale Engine House

Stonesdale which included the western extension of the Blakethwaite Vein.

At Stonesdale, Bradley sank a 45 fathom deep Engine Shaft to the Underset Chert and began driving a crosscut northwards to Blakethwaite Vein. An unexpected bonus was found after driving 217 fathoms, when the crosscut found a north-east to south-west vein which proved to be rich in the Main Chert. Because the crosscut rose and the beds dipped in the same direction, it cut the vein near the bottom of the Main Limestone. Drifts were driven for 28 fathoms west and 100 fathoms east, but, when Blakethwaite Vein was reached, it was found to be barren.

A water pressure engine, for pumping and winding, was installed in a massive masonry house at the shaft top. Water for the engine came in pipes from Foss Frith Tarn. In the shaft, which was partitioned and had wooden cage guides, were two lifts of pumps, each with 13 inch diameter pipes. Besides driving the pumps, the engine drove a winding drum, which lifted an iron cage.

In 1868, the mine, which produced 716 tons of ore between 1855 and 1860, was said to have been *"idle since 1861 – excepting the pumping of the engine and a little done now and again in repairs"*. It never reopened.

West Stonesdale Engine shaft - view of the balance bob chamber and shaft

Kisdon Mines

Kisdon is an impressive hill which is isolated by the river Swale on its north and east sides, and by the Skeb Skeugh on the west and south sides. The head waters of the latter stream, which joins the Swale at Muker, are at Keld. They are very near the Swale, but a little higher, which suggests that the river once flowed that way too. The Main Limestone and Chert, which form much of Kisdon's summit, are crossed by a number of weak veins, none of which were ever of any importance. There are few records of early workings, but Lord Wharton's miners were making trials there in 1715. Kisdon is not mentioned again, however, until the period 1816 to 1824, when nearly four tons of lead were made from ore raised there.

In August 1858 the Kisdon Mining Company, of which Sir George Denys was a director, took a 21 year lease of the area. Little is known of the company's early years, but at some time before 1866, James Kearton, who in 1851 was both publican of the Miners Arms at Muker and a lead miner, raised nearly two bings of ore.

In January 1866 the Kisdon Mining Company was incorporated as a limited liability company and began work in Myton Level, which was driven onto Myton's Vein. The 16 tons of ore raised by November gave the company an encouraging profit of £75, but the level soon broke into 'Old Man' workings. The vein became weaker and was very poor for ore, but nevertheless a few men were employed making trials until the winter of 1869-70.

The most southerly of the three, roughly east-to-west veins on the west side of Kisdon had also been tried from a level in the Underset Lime by John Alton. He drove 70 feet through broken ground before heavy rain caused a major collapse. A fresh start was made lower down the hill and by November 1866 Edmund Coates and sons had driven 43 feet of new level. They were soon troubled by water, however, which forced them to drive in the north wall of the vein. A rise through the Underset Limestone proved the vein to be full of clay and so the trial was abandoned and the men moved to Acre Walls Vein.

A number of 'Old Man' shafts had already tried Acre Walls Vein in the Main Limestone and so in March 1866 James Guy and partners began driving Guy's Level at the base of the Underset Limestone, soon cutting what they thought was Acre Walls Vein. As the level progressed, rises were put up to try the vein, which was from 18 to 24 inches wide and very poor. In January 1867 it was decided that they were not in Acre Walls Vein after all and a crosscut was driven to the north-east. This also failed to find the vein and, as the first vein had not improved, the level was abandoned in April 1868.

Another trial of Acre Walls Vein began in May 1866, when Miles Alderson and three partners began a hand level in the Main Limestone. By November the vein carried enough ore for the men to be put on bingtale, thus saving the company money. In December, however, they reached an 'Old Man' shaft and soon afterwards the ore gave out. The company kept the level going until October 1867 when, having never got clear of the 'Old Man', they gave up and moved the men to a new shaft much further along the vein. This trial also failed to find ore.

Not dismayed, the company set its men on sinking a shaft to try the vein in the Underset Limestone. When the bottom of the Main Limestone was reached at a depth of around 100 feet, however, a crosscut south from the shaft found that the vein was split up and gave no encouragement for sinking further. The crosscut was driven a little further, but it too was abandoned in August 1868.

Thomas Alderson and partners began reopening a shaft on a vein which crosses Kisdon's western flank in March 1866. This vein had been tried a few years earlier by Simon Alderson, who found a little ore. The shaft was sunk another seven fathoms, where a crosscut to the south soon found the vein and it was followed further into the hill until a cross vein was found. A sump was sunk on the junction and the new vein was followed eastwards. Some small, irregular patches of ore were found, but all the ground, being in the Main Chert, was badly broken. It was

decided, therefore, to abandon these lower levels and try the Black Beds from a new rise, but here, too, the ground was broken and the vein disturbed, so the men were moved to Morsgill Level in November 1867.

Morsgill Vein, which was thought to be the western continuation of the East Arngill Vein, was tried in the Main Limestone by a level which was begun by James Kearton and three partners in May 1866. Two bings of ore were raised in the early autumn, but the irregular bedding made the vein difficult to work. The miners also broke into 'Old Man' workings which, being hand-picked, were thought to date from the 17th century or even earlier. As might be expected, the ore had gone and a number of trials failed to find more. Sir George Denys became increasingly unhappy with the progress being made and, in November 1867, replaced James Kearton's partnership with Thomas Alderson's, who were paid on fathomtale. They continued driving the level, but found no ore and it was abandoned in June 1868.

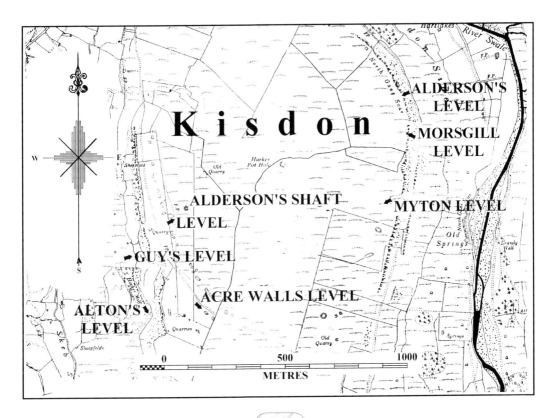

Faced with the failure of all its trials, time was running out for the Kisdon Mining Company. Nevertheless, it began what proved to be its last trial, on Alderson's Vein, in May 1868. Edmund Coates and Simon Alderson were given the job of driving a new level where the vein outcropped in the Main Limestone, at the north-west end of the hill. As before, the ground was poor and the level was driven in the vein's north cheek for most, if not all, of the 830 feet it was driven. The forehead was stopped early in 1869 and a nine fathom rise, to a 32 fathom long durk drift, was made to try the vein in the Main Chert. The ground was no more firm or productive here, however, and in January 1870 Sir George advised the company to suspend all its works. This was done and the decision was taken to dissolve the company on June 30th 1870. It was not quite the end, however, as another 11 cwts of ore were won from Myton Vein between August and October 1870, before the rails were taken up in 1871.

EWE SCAR AND ARN GILL MINES

When Christopher Lonsdale Bradley gave up the Blakethwaite, Lownathwaite and Swinnergill Mines in 1861, Sir George Denys took them over and worked them himself, first as the Blakethwaite Mining Company and then on his own behalf.

By the autumn of 1865, James Dunn and partners were driving Ewe Scar Level near Gunnerside Lodge. This was on the Sun Vein, which had not been worked before. The level was in sandstone, but the ground was very disturbed and was not expected to improve until the vein was followed eastwards towards its junction with Whitaside Vein. Some ore was produced, but work stopped early in 1869 and the rails were taken out in 1875.

East and West Arn Gill, on the east side of the Swale opposite Kisdon, are crossed by weak veins which run from north-west to south-east and have flots associated with them. Although the flots probably produced

bunches of ore, stories of finds valued at £12,000 have not been substantiated and should, perhaps, be dismissed.

As usual, the early history of these mines is patchy, but the first known working was in the 1750s, when three tons of ore were raised. Between 1812 and 1832 both the Arn Gills were part of Messrs Hopper's Swinnergill and Lownathwaite Mines. Their West Arngill Level was 129 fathoms long by 1816, but it is not mentioned in the closure report of 1832, which suggests that the mine had closed soon afterwards. This is confirmed by Sir George Denys' agent, Ralph Place, who, in 1866, proposed reopening the level which had been "*abandoned perhaps 50 years ago*" George Guy & company produced a further six tons of lead in 1835 and 1836.

In the early 1840s, Christopher Lonsdale Bradley drove a level in the upper part of the Main Limestone at East Arn Gill. This was onto a weak vein which runs south-east from Morsgill Mine on Kisdon. The vein here was loose and unproductive, according to Ralph Place, but rises into the overlying chert may have found some ore.

The longest period of working began in October 1865, when Sir George Denys' Blakethwaite Company reopened East Arn Gill and began getting ore from strings associated with the Old Vein in the Underset Limestone. In order to try the Sun Vein in the same bed, Adelaide Level was begun in the grit below the Main Limestone during 1866. A few men continued working until September 1870, when they were withdrawn. Thereafter, the levels were steadily stripped of their rails etc for use in the company's work at Swinnergill and Sun Hush Mines.

During 1919, Pickup and Fawcett reopened East Arngill Level and drained an '*Old Man's*' Sump, where ore had reputedly been left behind, using a syphon. They also sank a new sump in the vein and drove north for about 120 feet in the Underset Limestone looking for a flot. They failed to find one, however, and so drove the main level a few fathoms north-east before sinking again. This time, they soon cut a flot and produced about 23 tons of ore before it ran out. The partners gave up the mine in spring 1921.

Beldi Hill Mines

The Keldside North, Middle and Sun Veins cross the River Swale and run east across Hall Moor to the head of Swinnergill. Rose and Jarvis Veins run north-east after leaving the above veins at Oldfield Hush. The veins were all well placed for working from levels and produced ore from the Crow Beds down to the Underset Limestone.

The seeds of a long and acrimonious dispute over the ownership of this mine, now known as Beldi Hill, were sown in 1738 when the Trustees of the Duke of Wharton sold the manors of Healaugh and Muker to Thomas Smith. The ambiguous wording of the agreement, which only reserved the lead ore under the unenclosed wastes and common lands, led to disputes which were not settled until the 1770s. The following is an outline of a complex set of events.

In May 1738 the Trustees allowed Thomas Clarkson and Abraham Fryer to prospect for lead ore at Beldi Hill. They worked until December, when they gave up because no ore had been found. In 1742, however, when the old bargain expired, Thomas Smith leased Beldi Hill to two brothers, John and Thomas Parke, and Leonard Hartley for 21 years, claiming that it was part of the old enclosures. They sank a series of shafts on the North and Sun Veins, but soon found that pumps were needed. In order to drain the shafts, therefore, they drove the 1200 foot long Parkes Level from Swinnergill. This cost £300 and took nearly three years to cut Sun Vein near the boundary with the Trust's royalty. The level also drained the workings of Swinnergill Mine, but the Trustees refused to pay anything towards its cost. In the spring of 1751, therefore, Parkes' mine was declared to be worked out and the level mouth was dammed. Water was also turned into a shaft on North Vein, which quickly flooded Swinnergill Mine. The Trust's workmen destroyed the watercourses leading to the shaft and watchmen were set, with order to *"acquaint the agents with what they see done at different times"*. The flooding caused roof-falls in Swinnergill Mine, which also had to be cleared. The matter went unresolved and, on June 6th 1751, a bargain was let for a new level to drain the Trust's Sun Vein shafts. The level was 385 feet long and James Waggett and seven partners were paid £130 for working day and night, until September 24th 1752, to complete it.

In 1766, the Parkes sublet 10 Meers of ground near the Old Hush at Beldi Hill to John Scott & Company. They sank shafts onto the Sun Vein and between 1768 and 1771 smelted around 210 tons of lead per year at the Spout Gill Smelt Mill on the south side of Swaledale.

After the Trust was wound up, the mineral rights passed to Anna-Maria Draycott and, in 1768, her husband, the Earl of Pomfret, claimed the minerals at Beldi Hill. In preparation for a law suit, the Earl had affidavits taken from men who claimed knowledge of the Beldi Hill Mine. His miners also began sinking a shaft on the west side of the Old Hush on June 5th 1769. The following day, over 300 of Smith's supporters assembled at Beldi Hill and *"there unlawfully riotously and routously beet wound and illtreat him the said William I'Anson* [Pomfret's lawyer] *and did then and there*

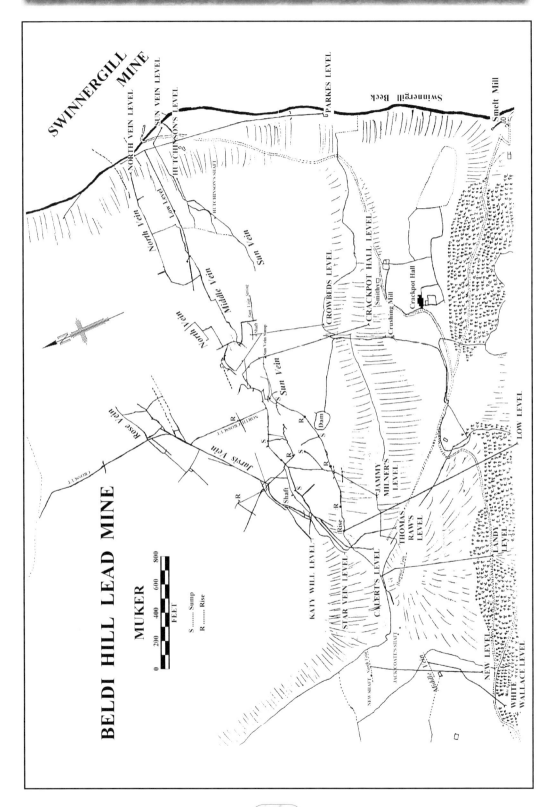

**Beldi Hill Smelt Mill
(YDNPA)**

*with great force and violence throw him...
into a certain place there nine yards deep
called a hush gutter"*. More of Pomfret's men
were thrown into the same place, including
three who were working in a shaft from which
they were pulled *"by the hair of their heads,
their arms and clothes"!* The shaft was filled
in, but work on it resumed a week later. Two
weeks after that, however, Parkes' men
flooded it.

Smith's smelt mill on Barney, or Old Gang,
Beck, between Pomfret's Surrender Mills and
Raygill Mill, had its water supply cut
repeatedly, and his smelters had to take the
bellows home with them to prevent their
being slashed. Pomfret seized Smith's Spout
Gill smelt mill, along with £2000 worth of

ore and slags, on June 26th 1769. He was
also granted an injunction preventing
interference with his mines, but not before
the Parkes had removed their ore.

The Assize Court at York ruled in Thomas
Smith's favour, but Pomfret was not satisfied
and took his cause to the Court of King's
Bench at Westminster, where he lost again.
He also lost a further three appeals to the
House of Lords, and by May 1772, John Scott
had recovered the Spout Gill Smelt Mill for
Smith. Finally, Pomfret was ordered to pay
Smith £400 in compensation for damage by
his men.

In order to avoid further problems, Smith
abandoned his two smelt mills and thereafter
ore from his mines was smelted at Beldi Hill

**Smithy near Crackpot
Hall (YDNPA)**

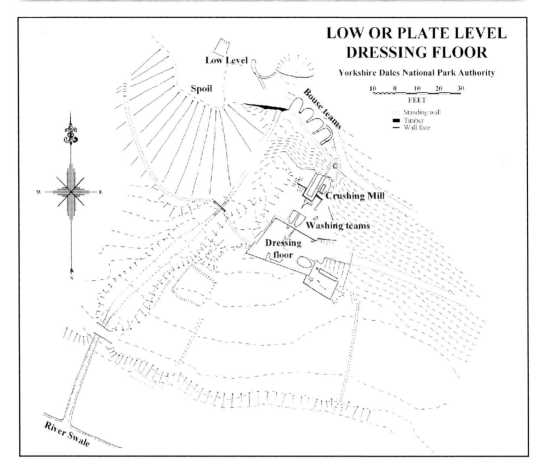

LOW OR PLATE LEVEL
DRESSING FLOOR

Yorkshire Dales National Park Authority

smelt mill, which had been built in 1771 at the foot of Swinnergill, near its junction with the Swale. This mill had a single ore-hearth, but was rebuilt around 1840 when a slag-hearth mill and a roasting furnace, in a detached building, were added. The short flue, which ran up a very steep crag to a chimney, was also built then. The mill's peat house stood about 300 feet to the west, alongside the track leading to the Low Level. Output from the Beldi Hill mines was low after 1860 and the smelt mill was used sporadically until it closed in 1883.

Some time before 1769, Thomas Raw's Level was driven to prove the junctions of Rose and Jarvis Veins with the North, Middle and Sun Veins. This area had already been tried by hushing and moderate amounts of ore had been found. Higher up the hush were Calvert's Level, driven onto Middle Vein, Star

Vein Level, on a north string of Middle Vein, and Katy Will Level.

From 1808 until the early 1830s Beldi Hill was worked by Hopper, Monkhouse & Company, who also worked the Swinnergill, Lownathwaite and Keldside Mines and had mines at Greenhow Hill, Sargill in Wensleydale and Lunehead in Teesdale. They were followed by Henry Alderson Monkhouse & Company from 1838 to 1849. Between them, the two companies drove eight levels into the network of veins and proved them from the Crowbeds down to the Undersets.

Crackpot Hall Level became the principal working in the Main Limestone, and eventually reached the mine's northern boundary. Its dressing floor had a waterwheel-powered roller crusher, and there was a smithy nearby. To the west, the veins were tried in the Main Limestone from Landy and

Aerial view of Low Level dressing floor (YDNPA)

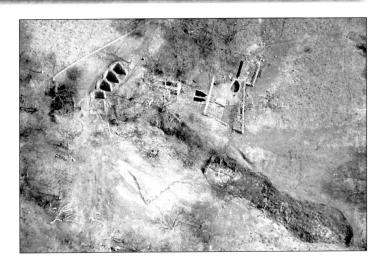

Low Level dressing floor - Site of Waterwheel-powered roller crusher washing kilns in background

New Levels, but with little apparent success. Their entrances, which are alongside the track leading from Keld to Crackpot Hall, are marked by runs of spoil, tipped down the steep hillside.

White Wallace Level and the Low, or Plate Holes, Level were both driven from near the River Swale to prove the Underset Limestone. The vein was barren at the former, but Low Level followed Sun Vein east as far as Crackpot Hall Level. It was also linked to Landy Level by the Golden Ball Rise. It was in this level, according to Fawcett, that, in 1882, after firing a shot two men heard *"the ominous rush of water in heavy volume"*. They had broken into flooded workings at Landy and *"quickly realizing their danger*

they rushed along the narrow durk drift, and down the rise to escape the flood. On reaching the bottom, the older man flung his younger companion into an empty waggon, and made for the entrance. This was barely reached before the water overtook them, but they just managed to escape being submerged, though the water filled more than half the depth of the level". When it subsided, the flood had filled the rise with *"stones and other debris, completely destroying it"*. The mine was abandoned soon afterwards.

Low Level had its own dressing floor with a waterwheel-powered roller crusher. The bouse teams and other structures on this dressing floor have been consolidated by the Yorkshire Dales National Park Authority.

Swinnergill Mines

The North, Middle and Sun Veins cross Swinnergill Beck from Beldi Hill into the AD Lessors' ground, where they soon run up against Field Marshall Vein, which runs west-north-west from Lownathwaite. In the 1780s, however, the three veins were believed to be the continuations of Fryerfold, Merryfield and Old Rake Veins respectively.

Sir Thomas Wharton's miners were working at Swinnergill in 1705, but the spur to activity was the driving of Parkes Level in the mid 1740s. When Parkes Level was blocked, as already described, the Trustees of the Duke of Wharton's estates drove their own level from near the waterfall at the junction of East Grain and Swinnergill. This was the Main, or Low Level, which begins on top of the Main Chert, but enters the Main Limestone because the veins have thrown the beds down to the south-west. The Trust's miners produced 370 tons of lead from the mine between 1751 and 1756.

A Captain Metcalfe was working the mine in 1787, when he had 23 meers (2070 feet) of ground running east from Swinnergill Beck. Beside the Main Level, a sketch plan of his workings shows three crosscuts driven to the veins from the side of East Grain. The lowest of these was probably Smiddy Level, driven from near the mine blacksmith's shop, and the highest was the Top Level to the Crow Beds. Metcalfe's ore was smelted at Lord Pomfret's Lownathwaite mill, which had been built on the western flank of Gunnerside Gill in 1769.

Until the end of the 18th century, the AD Lessors had either worked their own mines or let parts of veins to small groups of usually local men, for example Captain Metcalfe. This was fine until large developments, such as long horse levels, which soaked up vast amounts of cash, were needed. The answer was to lease large blocks of ground, with many veins, to partnerships of wealthy men. They took over the risk and, in return, paid a dead rent in cash, plus a fixed proportion of the ore raised as a duty or royalty.

One of the first such companies was headed by Thomas Hopper, a Newcastle lead merchant, and Teasdale Hutchinson, another lead merchant from Pateley Bridge. They leased Swinnergill Mine in July 1804, paying an annual rent of £50, rising to £100 when the mines became profitable, and 1/6th of all the lead produced. The company also rented Strands Hall, near Lodge Green, from Peter Denys and used it as its headquarters. In 1808 they also leased Thomas Smith's Beldi Hill Mines.

Their first ore was smelted at Beldi Hill Mill, but by the end of 1807 the company had opened its own smelt mill near the mine. This was a simple, two roomed building. In the bellows room was an 18 foot diameter waterwheel driving the bellows, and in the smelting room were two ore-hearths, set side by side. Fumes from the hearths were led into a short horizontal flue.

Swinnergill was not rich, however, and in August 1812 Hopper and Hutchinson took new partners, and Lownathwaite and the Arn Gills were added to their lease. By 1818 they had moved most of their smelting to Lownathwaite smelt mill. James Littlefair, the AD Lessors' agent, wrote in 1832 that Swinnergill Mill *"had not been in use for most*

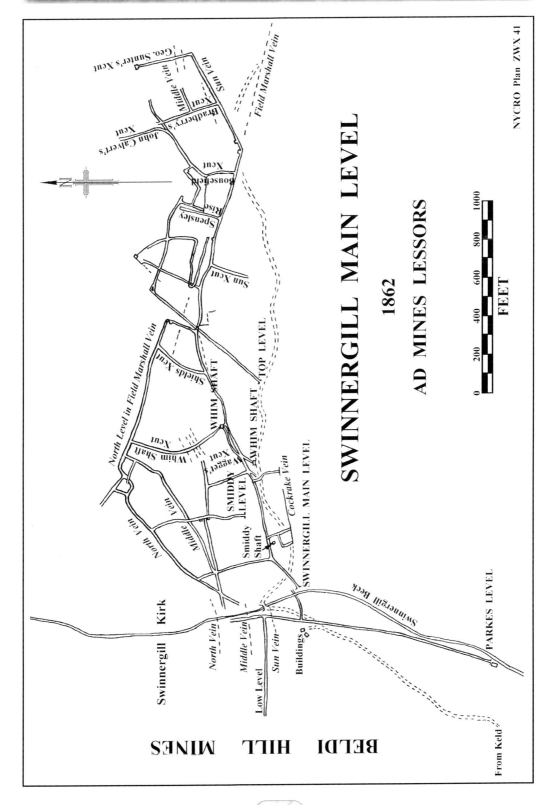

Swinnergill Smelt Mill (YDNPA)

part of 20 years. The horizontal chimney is much out of repair, also the roof of the mill."

Messrs Hopper gave up their Lownathwaite and Swinnergill Mines in 1832, having produced 1964 tons of lead. For a few years they were picked over by a small number of miners, but from 1837 both mines were added to Blakethwaite Mine and taken by a new company, which styled itself as the Strands Company. Between 1837 and 1861, therefore, the output from all three mines was lumped together. The Strands Company appears to have concentrated its efforts at Lownathwaite and Blakethwaite and it is not clear what, if anything, it did at Swinnergill.

In December 1861, soon after the Strands Company gave up its mines, the new Blakethwaite Company reopened Swinnergill Main Level and got some 360 tons of ore before closing the mine again in 1865.

When the AD Lead Mining Company Ltd reopened Swinnergill Mine in 1873, it also got permission to reopen Parkes Level in order to try the veins in the Underset Limestone. Parkes Level was driven to the Middle Vein and the rise between the two levels was repaired for ventilation. The trial was a failure, however, and the rails were taken out in 1877.

Lownathwaite Mines

Around 850 feet of strata, from the Howgate Edge Grit down to the Fifth Limestone, are exposed in Gunnerside Gill. The Main and Underset Beds outcrop high on the valley sides above Gunnerside and, owing to their steady dip northwards, might be expected to disappear quickly below the rising floor of Gunnerside Gill. They do not, however, because the vertical displacement of the veins which cross the gill near Lownathwaite causes them to be repeated.

Fryerfold and Old Rake Veins converge on Lownathwaite, where they are called North and Sun Vein respectively. These veins, which are associated with several strings and sub-veins, continue westwards to Swinnergill as Field Marshall Vein. They have been heavily mined on both sides of the gill and their gangue is principally barytes, with some fluorspar, witherite and calcite.

The landscape has been greatly changed by hushing, making it complex and difficult to understand. To do so, one has to work backwards from the three major hushes which now dominate the hillside. The southernmost hush, on Water Sykes Vein, merges with Sun, or Clifton, Hush. Then comes North Hush, which runs parallel to Sun Hush and extends right up the hill. The age of most of the hushes remains to be settled, but late 18th century plans of the area show lots of shafts where the hushes now are. Nevertheless, the bargain book also mentions hushes before then:-

"February 26th 1766. Then granted and let to Isaac Alderson & ptrs all the waste or rubage [rubbish/rubble] *which lies in the foot of Old Rake & Fryerfold Hushes from an old shaft last wrought by William Bell & ptrs, down to the beck side. And likewise all the rubage in the foot of Lownathwaite Hush, from the mouth of Clarkson's Level, to the beck. They are to have 8 shillings per horse* [2 cwts] *for all the ore they get from the said wastes. NB it is agreed to add all the ground in Old Rake Hush up to James Shaft to the above bargain."*

It is not clear when mining at Lownathwaite began, but in the 1670s Lord Wharton's partners were not eager to spend more money on trials there because of the extent of old workings. The trial went ahead, however, and in 1683 Philip Swale wrote of it:-

"For the leadwork we were in great hopes at Lownathwaite, finding good ore in driving up the level which is about 20 yards on the north of the old fore wrought rake; but have met with the 'Old Man', and fears he is gone with what we hoped would have repaid our great charge there that now we must be content to glean after him."

A report by Adam Barker suggests that the 'Old Man' had reached depths of around 240 feet and they were still troubled by his workings in March 1685 when they were making good progress with sinking a shaft because the weather had been dry.

"That they have opened the forefield shaft at Lownathwaite 17 fathoms, then come to a sump filled to [the] *top, but*

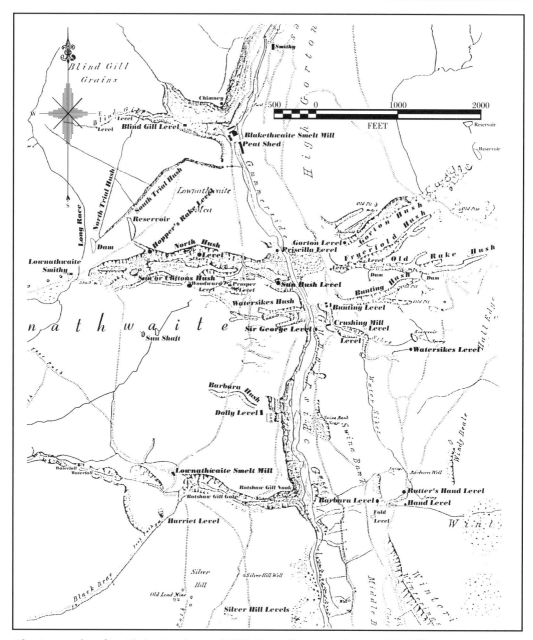

The Lownathwaite, Blakethwaite and Old Gary Mines on Gunnerside Gill

now opened 12 fathoms, and then come to another sump which they have opened 11 fathoms, but had not when he came thence soled it [got to the bottom], but hopes it may by this time. They found it very dacker of wind [poorly ventilated] that they took a fan down into the ground to help to wind which would not do, but was forced to carry down a pair of bellows and place likewise: the which, before he came away, did make help that they continued working, but how far the 'Old Man' has gone they could not tell, neither was they come to the vein but hopes in time (though uncertain when) to see how the 'Old Man' hath left that work."

The Lownathwaite mines were worked in a small way throughout most of the 18th century, and in 1742 the London Lead Company briefly considered leasing them from the Duke of Wharton's trustees. Their correspondence refers to the *"forefield of the Level of Lownathwaite"*, which shows that at least one level had been driven by then. This would not be a horse level, however, but merely a sough for draining and ventilating the workings. Its mouth was later destroyed by hushing.

With output from his Swinnergill and Lownathwaite mines rising, Lord Pomfret built a smelt mill on the north side of Botshaw Gill at Lownathwaite in 1769. George Jackson and Leonard Raw leased the mines there from Lord Pomfret in 1784, and George Raw's 1787 sketch plan of the area suggests that they concentrated on the North Vein, where he marked 14 shafts. What is now called Lownathwaite House was the mine smithy.

Not much is known about Lownathwaite mill, which was an oblong building, around 75 feet long by 30 feet wide, with a chimney directly over the two ore-hearths — as at Marrick High Mill. Jackson and Raw used the mill from 1784, and James Galway & Son built a washing floor there in 1805. Ore from Thomas Chippendale's Blakethwaite Mine was smelted there from 1806, and from around 1818 Chippendale shared the mill with Messrs Hopper. The latter party closed their smelt mill in Swinnergill soon after. The lack of a flue, for recovering particles of lead which were volatilized during smelting, was a major drawback and so a new mill, with a flue, was built at Blakethwaite in 1820 and Lownathwaite mill closed shortly afterwards.

Lownathwaite was in the hands of the mineral lords again by 1806, however, when the cost of driving Dolly Level appears in their fathom work accounts. This level was driven from Barbara Hush and proved Barbara and Spar Veins in the Main Limestone before it reached Lownathwaite.

Thomas Hopper and Company extended their lease to include all the mines, except Blakethwaite, west of Gunnerside Gill, and north from the River Swale in 1812. They continued driving Dolly Level, having changed its name to Barbara Level, and its forehead was 1600 feet from the mouth by October 1816. The level was then driven up to the third sump from Hopper's Low [later Priscilla] Level, on Lownathwaite North Vein, before turning westwards to prove the vein and a fault-feature called the Great Break.

Harriet and Silver Hill Levels, both near Botshaw Gill, were also driven by Hopper & Company to try Silver Hill Vein in the Main Limestone. Later, Silver Hill Low Level was driven to try the vein in the Underset Limestone.

Also around this time, Woodward's Level was driven west from the junction of Water Sykes and Sun Hushes to their junction with North Vein. Prosper Level, about which nothing is known, was driven from Sun Hush about 40 feet lower than Woodward's Level.

Hopper's Rake Level was driven from the north side of North Vein, nearly opposite the point where Water Sykes Vein enters it, in search of the latter's continuation. It found a vein bearing around 20 degrees more to the north than Water Sykes. It was first called Hopper's Rake, but later it became Blind Gill Vein and it is sometimes called Water Sykes Vein. This vein had been proved by the North and South Trial Hushes, which run towards Blakethwaite Smelt Mill from the dam on the north side of the North Hush, at NY933015. In 1816 it was proposed to drive a level from the North, or Blind, Gill *"for the top sets in Hopper's Rake Vein"*. Nothing was done until 1842, however, when Blind Gill Level was begun.

Barbara Level found ore in Main Limestone at Lownathwaite and, probably encouraged by this, the company began driving Priscilla Level west from near the beck in Gunnerside Gill. This level, which reached the North Vein after a short distance as a crosscut in the footwall, was begun in the 27 Fathom Grit, below the Underset Limestone. It was also well sited for sending ore to Blakethwaite mill. The results, coupled with the major slump which began in 1829, were disappointing however, and production fell rapidly from 1830.

Hopper & Co. gave up when their lease ended in 1832, but the mines were kept ticking over by the mineral lords until a new lessee could be found. Teams of miners, with strict instructions to keep the rails, waggons etc in good order, were allowed to work parts of Barbara Level. Others worked in Clifton Hush, Woodward Level and on the North Vein near the smithy at Lownathwaite.

Both Lownathwaite and Blakethwaite mines were leased to a new company, which styled itself the Strands Company, in 1836. This was after a house called Strands, about one mile east of Gunnerside, which was owned by the mineral lords and had been used by Messrs Hopper.

The Strands Company began Blind Gill Level in 1842 and drove it westwards to cut Blind Gill Vein in the Main Limestone. The vein produced ore as it was followed northwards, but after 500 feet the Main Limestone dipped below the level and the workings were eventually drowned out.

The Old Gang Lead Mining Company Ltd reopened the level in March 1895 and began driving John Reynoldson's Crosscut west. This was to try some strings, in the Main Limestone, which ran parallel to Blind Gill Vein and had been cut by Sir Francis Level in lower strata. Because it was in limestone, however, the crosscut was very hard to drive and so it was abandoned in December 1898 after having been driven for 360 feet, at a cost of £600, without finding a vein.

The Strands Company also drove Priscilla Level westwards on the North Vein to the Great Break Vein, which throws the beds down to the west by 175 feet, and then for a further 570 feet on top of the Main Limestone. The vein here must have been unpromising and no attempt was made to work it from Swinnergill either.

The same company began Sun Hush Level from a point in Sun Hush which was about

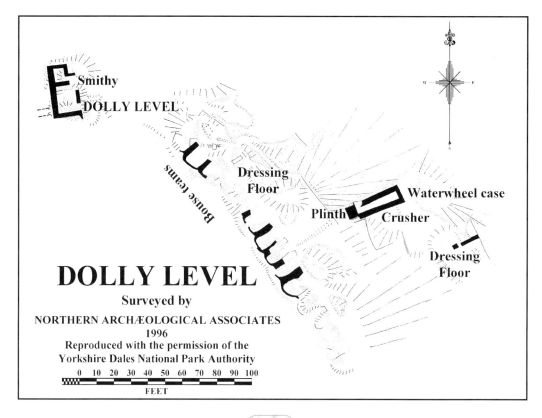

Smithy

DOLLY LEVEL

Bouse teams

Dressing Floor

Plinth   Crusher

Waterwheel case

Dressing Floor

DOLLY LEVEL

Surveyed by
NORTHERN ARCHÆOLOGICAL ASSOCIATES
1996
Reproduced with the permission of the
Yorkshire Dales National Park Authority

0   10   20   30   40   50   60   70   80   90   100

FEET

Waterwheel case at Dolly (Barbara) Level, Lownathwaite (YDNPA)

50 feet higher than Priscilla Level. Owing to the veins' vertical displacement, however, it was also just below the Underset Limestone. It was driven on Middle Vein, Metcalfe's Sun Vein and then Lownathwaite Sun Vein for at least 2400 feet. The bouse teams for the level were built into the confines of the hush in a V shape from the level mouth, but, owing to erosion, little remains of them or the dressing floor, except part of the pit for the waterwheel which drove the roller crusher.

When the Strands Company, under Christopher Lonsdale Bradley, gave up in 1861, Sir George Denys kept the mines ticking over, first as the Blakethwaite Mining Company and then on his own behalf. After 1864, some of Sir George's men were involved in driving Sir Francis Level (see below), a deep trial which opened the last period of mining at Lownathwaite. In order to exploit the new ground being opened by this level, the AD Lead Mining Company Ltd, with Sir George Denys as its managing director, leased all the ground west of Gunnerside Gill in 1873. In October 1873 it

began repairing Priscilla Level, which had been idle for some time, and laying rails, some 3770 feet of which were stripped from Blakethwaite Level. Men were also set to work in Sun Hush, at Barbara Level (which was called Dolly Level again) and at Swinnergill. In May 1874, Sir George wrote that Dolly Level was open *above the Sun Hush Level forehead for 200 fathoms up to the Great Break and more than 100 fathoms beyond. Priscilla Level is now believed to be driven under Dolly up to the Coal Shaft and beyond.* By February 1876, Priscilla Level was open to the foremost sump from Dolly Level, 600 feet beyond the Great Break.

As well as clearing the level westwards, miners began to drive north from Priscilla Level on Blind Gill Vein. Good ore was found in a rise to the Underset Limestone in March 1876, and men from other parts of the mines were set to work raising it. Sir George also noted that *Place's Crosscut from Sun Hush Level stopped 10 years ago when within two fathoms of Blind Gill Vein*.

The remaining work on Watersikes and

Waggon body at the mouth of Priscilla level

Keystone from Priscilla level

Blind Gill veins was done from Priscilla and Sir Francis Levels between 1877 and 1906. It is, therefore, dealt with in the section relating to Sir Francis Level.

SIR FRANCIS LEVEL

Most of the area's mines were impoverished by the late 1850s, and so plans were made for a trial of the Third and Fourth Limestones in the area where the Fryerfold and Old Rake Veins cross Gunnerside Gill. To do this, the Sir Francis Level was driven from a spot in the gill about 4400 feet to the south, which allowed the miners to take advantage of easier

driving in the shale between the Fourth and Fifth Limestones.

It was Sir George Denys' belief that this new level, named after his son and heir and begun in June 1864, would provide work for the next generation. It was to follow the boundary between the Blakethwaite and Old Gang Companies, which shared the cost of driving in the ratio of 1/5th to 4/5ths respectively, and was expected to take around 15 years to reach the vein.

The Blakethwaite Company gave up in December 1866 and the Old Gang Company continued the level on its own. At first, the level had advanced nearly seven feet per week using hand-bored shotholes and black powder blasting, but this fell to under three feet after three years. The cost of driving also rose steadily and had reached £8 5s 0d per fathom by December 1866. It was £8 10s 0d per fathom in July 1869, but it had been £10 for a time, showing that harder rocks were being cut. Fresh air was piped from a waterblast in one of the two shallow air shafts. When Sir George suggested using compressed air drills to speed up progress in 1869, the company was reluctant, so he became a contractor and drove the level himself, using Haupts Improved Rock Drills. He also paid 1/5th of the costs. The company paid him £8 10s 0d per fathom and provided the rails, waggons, air pipes etc. It also built the watercourse which brought water to the waterwheel-driven air compressor in an engine house at the mouth of Sir Francis Level. Sir George described that plant as follows:-

Buidings at Sir Francis Mine, c1965

"The motive power was water, brought to bear upon a wheel 28 feet in diameter, and 4 feet wide, attached to one of Low's improved double cylinder air compressors of high pressure with a wrought iron receiver and connections made by E.R. & W. Turner of Ipswich, which worked up to about 60 lbs pressure on the inch".

Compressed air boring began on January 26th 1870 and, once the men had learned to use the borers and any teething problems were settled, John Calvert, a Gunnerside blacksmith, was given the job of maintaining the machinery. Apart from breakdowns, progress was slow because the level was also in a bed of hard grit, and costs began to mount. Sir George pushed on, noting that:-

"A man must pay for his experience in boring as in anything else. It is the opinion of all the men employed, and of the agents, that it would not have been possible for several hundred fathoms to have moved the forehead at a less price than from £12 to £14 a fathom by hand labour."

Mouth of Sir Francis Level, c1965

One benefit of using the borers was that the exhaust air ventilated the level forehead and allowed the men to work without the need for air shafts. This saved both time and money. After experiments with gun-cotton instead of black powder, for blasting, dynamite was introduced in March 1873. This increased the rate of advance.

Fryerfold Vein was cut on Monday March 12th 1877, after 13 years of driving. Some ore was found and Sir George Denys was ebullient. In May the Old Gang Company began a rising in the vein near where it had been cut, but it was poor. It then drove the level eastwards, along Old Rake and Fryerfold Veins, for about 180 feet and found good ore, but the bearing beds went deeper. By October 1889 the forehead in the Old Rake was 2325 feet east of Sir Francis Level.

To the west, the ore soon gave out, but the vein improved after 160 feet, and there was ore both above and below the level in the AD ground. By the end of August 1878, the AD Company had raised 480 tons of ore and things looked promising. A sump was sunk to work the ore under the level and in April 1879 Sir George wrote that:-

> *"In the Engine Sump, Fifth Lime cut 11 fathoms below the rails on the north, or high, side. There are 27 fathoms of grit and plate between the Fourth and Fifth Limes. Vein eight feet wide. On the south cheek is a solid rib of ore three to four inches wide. The low price of lead, however, spoils the whole job, and if it continues must eventually ruin both the AD Co. and Old Gang as well."*

In June the bank refused the money to pay the AD Company's wages bill, but then relented. In August the company and its bankers agreed to finish the Engine Sump and install water pressure engines supplied by Hathorn, Davy & Company, of Leeds. The Old Gang Company, however, refused to share in this scheme, preferring instead to sink its own sump and drive the main level

Air receiver at mouth of Sir Francis Level, 1976

eastwards. In order to drain this sump, it borrowed a water-pressure-driven donkey engine from the AD Company. This left it very exposed, because the loan would end when the water supply was needed for the AD engines. Work on the underground engine chamber began on August 1st 1879 and was completed on September 2nd 1880, when:-

> *"We had a festival at Sir Francis to commemorate the event. Speeches, songs, band of music, 30 gallons of beer and miners all very happy."*

Sir George, who died in February 1881 and never saw his scheme at work, estimated that the engine house, sump, rises, watercourses, dams etc had cost nearly £1200. With the engines, it eventually cost £4500.

The AD Engine Sump was 127 feet deep, leaving it just short of the Fifth Limestone on the vein's south cheek, and the winding engine was in place by November 1880.

Around the New Year, the donkey engine was taken out of the Old Gang Sump and the water rose until it was within 18 feet of the top. The men had been driven out of the sump by February 1881, when the AD Company was preparing to connect the pressure mains from the surface to its engines, as well as putting in the cages and guides and fixing the sheaves for the ropes. The sump was ready to work until July, however. A problem with sand and grit in the feed water, which damaged the engine's valves, was solved by making a filter from heather and placing it across the intake at the reservoir.

Good ore was found where the Fifth Lime, with grit above it, was on the vein's north cheek. It was worked from Tiplady's Drift, at a depth of 80 feet, and stoped up to the level. The ore began to fail in April 1882, however, leaving the company without money to carry on. It stopped the engines that summer, allowing the sump to flood and, apart from some pumping in 1890 (see below), they have not worked since. Work on

driving the Sir Francis Level forehead was also stopped on September 11th 1882, and the men were set to work raising whatever ore there was in sight.

The AD Company was going broke, and early in 1884 its assets were seized and put into liquidation by the debenture holders. The Old Gang Company was also having problems and demanded a reduction in royalties, threatening to give up the mine if the lessors did not concede. Sir Francis Denys refused, however, and the company continued under the old terms.

Frank Raw, the AD agent, had begun a rise to Priscilla Level to drain the bearing beds, which dipped below it. After rising some 90 feet and driving 120 feet, a surveying error was discovered which meant that the rise was in the Sun Vein and not the North Vein as thought. In January 1884 Raw was succeeded by John Reynoldson who drove a crosscut to the North Vein where a new rise was begun. It did not hole into Priscilla Level until January 1885.

Water pressure winding engine at Sir Francis Level, 1976

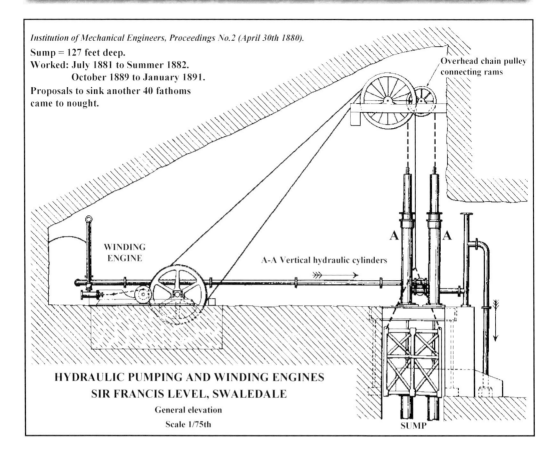

Institution of Mechanical Engineers, Proceedings No.2 (April 30th 1880).

Sump = 127 feet deep.
Worked: July 1881 to Summer 1882.
       October 1889 to January 1891.
Proposals to sink another 40 fathoms
came to nought.

Overhead chain pulley
connecting rams

WINDING
ENGINE

A-A Vertical hydraulic cylinders

A   A

HYDRAULIC PUMPING AND WINDING ENGINES
SIR FRANCIS LEVEL, SWALEDALE
General elevation
Scale 1/75th

SUMP

To save money, Sir Francis Level was stopped and the company concentrated on raising ore in Priscilla Level. The Old Gang directors surrendered their lease in December 1887 and, except for a few partnerships gleaning a living amongst the old works, the mines were idle for a time.

The Old Gang Lead Mining Company Ltd was formed to work the combined Lownathwaite and Old Gang setts in 1889. It had a capital of £20,000, but £2500 of this went on buying plant from the old companies. Another £5500 in shares went to the AD Company's debenture holders, whilst £3600 of shares remained unsold. The company lacked money from the start.

Sir Francis Level was driven north in Watersikes Vein, but after 1140 feet the vein died out, so the level was driven north-east, as a crosscut in the Fourth Lime, to Blind Gill Vein. The going was very hard, but, when the

vein was cut in March 1894, it was between three and four feet wide and carried some ore. In the hope of finding ore in the 10 Fathom Grit, a rise to Priscilla Level was begun, but it was stopped in March 1895, after getting up 180 feet, because the vein was barren. The miners were taken to Blind Gill Level, where they began driving John Reynoldson's Crosscut.

In the autumn of 1889, the new company began cleaning all the machinery in the engine house, in preparation for sinking the Engine Sump another 240 feet to try the deepest beds. In November the engine was said to be *"working day and night and pumping fairly well"*, but by January 1890 the agent wrote that *"the hydraulic engine is not being worked at present on account of the watercourses not being in good order"*. It was pumping again by May, but further repairs, costing £350, were needed. In November 1890, they had *"got the hydraulic machinery into proper*

Water pressure winding engine at Sir Francis Level, 1976

but, owing to the beds dipping (about 1 in 24) in the direction being driven, this strata was in the roof on the west side by July 1891 and had let in a lot of water.

In the spring of 1900, the company began *"opening out Blind Gill Level so as to ascertain the state Bradley left it and if possible sink from the level sole in search of ore"*. In 1892, it began a rise from Priscilla Level to drain a flooded sump in Blind Gill Level, 132 feet above. When the miners were *"within four or five feet of the sump there were signs of the water being loosed and the men made their escape to the rise, but before reaching it the water came with such velocity that it blew from three to four feet of vein clean out the height of the drift"*. Amazingly, no one was hurt.

Most of the ore raised between 1897 and 1899 came from Blind Gill Vein, in the Underset Limestone, and was dressed near the

working order and have placed six men to sink deeper in North Vein to prove the 5th Sett Lime on south side". Nevertheless, in January 1891 *"one of the bottom clacks in the working barrel failed to lift the water, thus causing the water to rise before it could be changed. This and the scarcity of water (through severe frost) for working the engine compelled us to abandon our sinking operations at present"*. In the event, the trial was abandoned before sinking began. The frost during the winter of 1890/91 was so bad that the company was unable to use the compressor and had to resort to hand drilling, with a consequent rise in costs to 90 shillings per fathom.

After these failures, the company concentrated on driving Priscilla Level north on Blind Gill Vein, which it had been doing since August 1889. At the latter date, the level was in the grit below the Underset Limestone,

Cage at the sump head, Sir Francis Level, 1976

mouth of Priscilla Level. In 1899, however, Cyprian Rutter's and Frank Barker's Rises to Blind Gill Level showed the vein to be barren in the Main Limestone. When the Underset Limestone dipped below the Priscilla soles in 1900, it was too wet to be worked from sumps. The vein was poorer in the Underset Chert, which went below Priscilla Level sole around June 1901. Work was stopped, therefore, and *"good ore was left in the forehead, but we were unable to get it for the water"* until Sir Francis Level could be brought up to drain it.

Preparations for resuming the rise from Sir Francis Level to Priscilla Level, which was

Falling main, taking water to S.F. Engines

stopped in 1895, began in March 1899. The air compressor was also repaired. The work, which was very wet, did not begin until March 1901, however, and holed to Priscilla on June 26th that year.

Sir Francis Level was driven north-west in Blind Gill Vein from October 1900, but the vein, which carried a little ore and had the Fourth Lime on its west side and gritstone on its east side, failed about 800 feet beyond the rise. A crosscut was driven north-east, through very hard rock, to the east cheek of Blind Gill Vein, which carried some ore. After following the vein for 80 feet, another rise to Priscilla Level was started. The forehead of Sir Francis Level was stopped on January 20th 1904, after being driven 30 feet beyond the rise to give standing space for empty waggons.

The Old Gang Lead Mining Company Ltd

had driven Priscilla Level for 1290 feet north-west along Blind Gill Vein by 1903, when a rise was begun near the forehead. This rise was 72 feet high and in the 10 Fathom Grit when, on March 8th 1904, there was a firedamp explosion. Such events were previously unknown in the district, and the two miners in the rise were not badly injured. Water entered the rise after 90 feet, making it very wet, and the men, even in oil skins, were soon soaked to the skin. More water was released when the Underset Lime was cut, and the rise was holed to Priscilla Level in April 1905. Ore from the soles was dressed at the level mouth, but after 300 feet the vein was too poor to pay costs and the men were transferred to the Old Rake Sun Vein, in Hard Level, on February 7th 1906. This ended lead mining in Gunnerside Gill.

The buildings associated with Sir Francis Level included a stable, a blacksmith's shop and an office. From 1869, a building near the level mouth housed a waterwheel-driven compressor and an air receiver. Both the AD and Old Gang companies built dressing floors in the valley below the mine. The former company's dressing floor was built on the west bank of the gill in 1876. It reputedly cost over £1250, about 1/5th of which went on three circular buddles. In 1878 a new bouse team was lined with planks and a railway laid to it. A railway was also built to the grinding mill.

Much of the equipment was scavenged from local mines. For example, the crushing mill rolls and chat mill, complete with a 20 foot diameter by four foot wide waterwheel, came from Keldside Mine, as did 300 feet of wooden launders. The 28 foot diameter waterwheel from the dressing floor at the West Stonesdale Mine was used to drive the hotching tubs.

The slimes were treated in circular buddles, driven by small waterwheels. There were two buddles on the first waste dressings, and one on the second waste dressings. The buddle floors sloped gently down from the centre boss to the circumference. The slimes, in a gentle stream of water, entered the buddle at its centre and were spread out by the flow

The AD dressing floor at Sir Francis Level, 1976

and the action of mechanical brushes. This separated the particles according to their densities and they accumulated in broad rings. When the buddle was full, the material nearest the centre of the buddle was clean ore and it was sent for smelting. The lightest material, which had little or no ore, collected near the circumference, and was thrown away. The intermediate material, which was a mix of ore and waste, was saved for further buddling or treatment in a dolly tub.

Dirty water from the floors was usually led into a settling pit, where any fine sediment was allowed to settle out. This deposit also contained some very fine ore which was recovered in a dolly tub.

The Old Gang Company's dressing floor was lower down the valley in order to get enough water. It was similar to the AD floor and, by the end of 1880, was estimated to have saved 46 per cent on dressing costs when compared to older methods. Just as it did in the mine, however, the Old Gang Company relied on the AD Company for its water supply. The ill-feeling between them surfaced

in the summer of 1882, when the AD men diverted the water off the Old Gang Company's launder, stopping the machinery and forcing the dressers to go home early. A letter to Sir Francis Denys complained of this deed and reminded him that their *"agreement was that the Old Gang dressing floors below AD's should have all the water after it had passed over AD's wheel."*

There were proposals for building a new, joint smelt mill in or near Gunnerside Gill, because most of the saving in dressing costs were lost in carrying their ore to the smelt mills, but the poverty of both companies ruled this option out. The AD Company used the old and inefficient Blakethwaite mill at first, but then used Surrender mill, about three-and-a-half miles to the east. The cost of carriage to Surrender was 14 shillings per ton of lead, which made it more profitable, by around 7s 11d per ton, to sell the ore direct to the smelters. It is said that the Old Gang Company carried its ore through Bunting Level and out of Hard Level, at a cost of 12 shillings per ton of lead.

Blakethwaite Mine

The eastern end of the Blakethwaite Vein, which is called Bishop Vein, was being worked near the head of Little Punchard Gill in 1710. Because of the mine's remoteness, however, little was done here until after 1797, when it became part of William Chaytor's Surrender Mine. Ore was then raised from a number of deep shafts, and Lonsdale's Level, which had been driven from the side of Blakethwaite Beck to prove the vein in the Crow Beds, was repaired.

In July 1806 Blakethwaite was leased to Thomas Chippendale and company, for 21 years, at an annual rent of £50 and a duty of 1/5th of the lead produced. They built an office near the foot of Cross Gill and drove the Low Level in the 10 Fathom Grit from nearby. A Top Level, which probably cut the vein in the Crow Limestone, was also driven at the top of the 10 Fathom Grit.

In August 1812, the company agreed a new lease, at a duty reduced to 1/6th, in return for driving Blakethwaite Level under the Main Limestone at Eweleap Scar. This level, which was to be "6 *feet by 3 feet and to be walled and arched with stone where needed*", was intended to prove the vein in the Main Limestone. Owing to the northwards dip of the strata, however, the limestone was below the level when it reached Blakethwaite Vein

after 2430 feet. Nevertheless, it was followed eastwards for 1800 feet and extensively stoped above and below the level.

The company had also begun driving Blakethwaite Low Level, from even lower down the gill, by May 1814 and was granted a ten year extension to its lease as an encouragement. This level still had about 3600 feet to drive in 1814, but had been abandoned by March 1818 when the ten year extension was surrendered.

The first vein cut by Blakethwaite Level was an extension of Rigg Vein, which the miners

Blakethwaite Dam

called Red Sun Vein. It was November 1818, however, before the level reached Blakethwaite Vein. Annual production averaged 383 tons of lead between 1820 and 1831, but then fell sharply as the result of a major price slump between 1830 and 1831, together with the end of the lease falling due in 1833.

A drift also followed Red Sun Vein north-west to its intersection with Blakethwaite Vein. It was near this point that an underground shaft, called the Pump (or East Engine) Sump, was sunk to a depth of 204 feet from the level. This had a sub-level at 50 feet, which worked the Main Limestone, and another at 192 feet in the Underset Limestone. An underground waterwheel, 29 feet in diameter by three feet breast, worked four-inch-square wooden rods connected to pumps in the shaft bottom. The same wheel also drove winding machinery which held 300 feet of galvanised flat iron rope, 2 inches wide by 5/8ths of an inch thick.

It is likely that most of the ore won between 1820 and 1831 came from the eastern end of the Blakethwaite Vein, especially the Pump Sump. The company built a dressing floor, with waterwheel-powered crushing rollers, near the entrance of Blakethwaite Level. It is likely that hand-operated hotching tubs, trunk buddles and dolly tubs were also used to dress the ore.

Chippendale's company surrendered its lease and in April 1836 all the ground from Gunnerside Beck westwards to Stonesdale Beck was leased to the

Blakethwaite smelt mill and penthouse (YDNPA)

Blakethwaite mill, 1946

*Blakethwaite
seat house, 1946*

Strands Company. It began smelting ore in June 1837 and soon had production back to and above its former levels, averaging 580 tons of lead per year between 1839 and 1847. This figure, of course, includes the Lownathwaite mines.

Blakethwaite Vein was followed westwards, but the beds dipped below the level until it was in shale and the vein became barren. To recover the vein, in 1841 the West Engine Sump was sunk to the top of the Underset Limestone, at a depth of 240 feet. A Whitham's water-pressure engine, with a 13 inch diameter cylinder, was built in a zinc lined chamber, said to have been lit by a large chandelier, at the shaft top.

The water which drove the engine was taken along Lonsdale's Level from the Blakethwaite dams and fed into a 160 feet high falling main. The engine, which began work in early 1842, drove two eight-inch pumps and a winding drum which could lift five hundredweights at a time.

The level from the foot of the West Engine Sump followed the vein westwards for 2450 feet, but it was given up in 1850 owing to the amount of water entering the workings. This coincided with Christopher Lonsdale Bradley's leasing ground in Stonesdale which included the western extension of the Blakethwaite Vein.

In his evidence to the Kinnaird Commission in 1863, Sir George Denys said that "*about a year ago*" he had taken Blakethwaite over and was working it "*with some other gentlemen*" because "*it was thrown on his hands*". This was the Blakethwaite Mining Company, and most of its 60 to 70 men were producing ore from Sun Hush and Blind Gill Levels at Lownathwaite. Some ore may also have been got in the old stopes above Blakethwaite Level, but no work appears to have been done in either sump.

The company's mines were extremely poor by December 1866, when it gave up, but Sir George Denys kept a few miners at work between 1867 and 1873. They were probably at Lownathwaite and Sir Francis Level. When the AD Lead Mining Company Ltd took over the mines in December 1873, one of its first tasks was to strip the rails from Blakethwaite Level.

Between 1888 and 1906 Blakethwaite was included in the lease of the Old Gang Lead Mining Company Ltd, which was driving Sir Francis Level along Blind Gill Vein towards its supposed junction with the Blakethwaite Vein near the spot where work stopped in 1860. This point was never reached, however, and there is no evidence that the company ever reopened Blakethwaite Level.

Chippendale & Company smelted its ore at Lownathwaite mill from 1806, but in 1819 output began to rise sharply and a new mill was built on a compact site at the confluence of the Blind Gill and Blakethwaite becks. In the summer of 1820, the road from Gunnerside to Lownathwaite was extended to the new mill, which began smelting in May 1821. This event was reported as follows:-

> *"Blakethwaite Co. have begun smelting with one ore-hearth but cannot make a push for one month because the calcining furnace is not ready."*

An agreement of some form, but it is not clear what, must have existed between the Blakethwaite Company and Messrs Hopper. They had shared Lowna–thwaite mill, and from 1824, when that mill closed, Hopper's ore was smelted at Blakethwaite mill. Moreover, the iron columns used to support the arches for the ore-hearths at Blakethwaite were similar to those at Hopper's Cockhill mill, on Greenhow Hill. Another link between the two companies was their agent, Nathan Newbould.

Fumes from the two ore-hearths were collected into a flue which ran to a chimney on top of the crags behind the mill. In 1864, a further 350 feet of flue, leading to a new chimney behind the crag, were built. The bellows, which blew the ore-hearths, were driven by an 18 feet diameter by three feet breast waterwheel, with *"wooden arms and shields and wooden shaft* [axle]". A room on the east side of the mill housed the calcining or roasting furnace, referred to above.

A peat house, for storing the peat to be burned in the hearths, stood across the beck from the mill. It was around 33 feet long by 10 feet wide and was roofed in local flagstone. Access to it was by a small bridge. Peat, which was cut on the moor near the chimney, was sent to the mill on a "Peat Slide", which ran

down the steep hillside about 200 feet west of the flue.

After the Strands Company gave up in 1861, the mill smelted ore for the Blakethwaite and Kisdon mining companies, as well as for Sir George Denys. It was probably idle from the end of 1870 until late 1873, when the AD Lead Mining Company took over, but closed for good in early 1878, because it was in bad repair and inefficient, and smelting was moved to the company's Surrender smelt mill. The mineral lords kept Blakethwaite mill in repair until 1914, when the roof, which had become unsafe, was taken off and sold to John Dougill, a local builder, for £21.

Ore-hearths at Blakethwaite smelt mill, c1964

The Old Gang Mines

Having dealt with the mines on the west side of Gunnerside Gill, let us now turn to those on the east side of the gill. They are part of what, in the 19th century, became the Old Gang Mines and cover the area east from Gunnerside Gill to a little east of Barney Beck. This ground was crossed by a number of veins, the most important of which were the Fryerfold, Merryfield, North Rake, Old Rake and Watersikes Veins.

The earliest miners probably got most of their ore in the Crow Limestone and Cherts, at a depth of around 140 feet, but in the 18th century they were able to get down into the Main Chert and the top of the Main Limestone by using whim shafts. Some of these were up to 390 feet deep and, until the various horse levels were driven, their ore was dressed at the shaft tops.

Gorton, Fryerfold, Old Rake and Bunting Veins outcrop in Gunnerside Gill and were worked by hushing before the end of the 18th century, but this work must have stopped earlier than it did at Lownathwaite because a number of levels were driven on these veins by the early 1800s. For example, Gorton

Bunting Level-tips, smithy and house teams, 1976

Level was driven onto Gorton Vein, which runs on the north side of Fryerfold Vein, probably a little before 1800. Gorton Level and another level below it are very inconveniently sited, being driven onto the vein outcrop from a very precipitous place. It is likely that little attention was paid to them once Bunting Level was into Fryerfold Vein, and in 1824 they had been abandoned for many years.

In 1805, John Davies, the AD Lessor's agent, wrote that a proposed crushing mill at Gorton Level was delayed because:-

"John Seare is dead who was your mill wright, he having a bargain of the putting up the mill at Gorton Level and he having had but poor health all this winter, by which he disappointed me in getting forward with that mill."

Owing to the steepness of the ground at Gorton Level, it is likely that the chosen site was nearer to what became Bunting Level dressing floor and that the first dressing floor at Bunting was built soon after the above note.

Bunting Level, with its prominent tip and fine set of bouse teams, was the main working on this side of the gill. It is not known precisely when the level was begun, but it may have been early in 1802, when John Davies moved from the Caldbeck Fell Mines to become agent for the AD Lessors. This level was driven in the shale bed below the Underset Limestone, on the line of the Bunting Strings which converge with the Old Rake as they go eastwards. It also worked Fryerfold Vein from a north crosscut, and Watersikes Vein from a south crosscut. It was driven from the lowest convenient position, without having to cut into the precipitous valley side. It is said to have been driven to *"drain the Underset of Merryfield*

Vein, but by* [John Davies'] *mismanagement was allowed to rise more than the whole height of the Undersets which are under water as much as if the level had never been driven"*. Certainly, when the Bunting Level forehead in Old Rake was connected to the drift from Hard Level, in 1828, Bunting was the higher by 24 feet.

When Messrs Alderson took the Old Gang Mines in 1811, they continued the level, but were troubled by *'Old Man'* workings. This is probably why Frederick Hall stopped the forehead in December 1814, soon after taking over as manager. Some ore was got in July 1814, but in 1824 the mine was neglected and in a poor condition.

One of the requirements of the lease granted to Jaques & Company in 1828 was that Bunting and Hard Level be driven towards each other. As noted above, however, there was a vertical difference of 24 feet between them when they met, and so hoppers were built into the rise. These were called the 'Metal Hoppers', but this is unlikely to mean that they were made of metal, rather that they were used to store dressed ore, which was colloquially known as 'Metal'. This gives strength to the story that dressed ore was taken through Bunting Level and brought out of Hard Level.

When Jaques & Company renewed their

Bunting Level-wheel case for grinding mill, (YDNPA)

by the '*Old Man*' because of the expense of crushing it using hammers. James Littlefair cites an example of this when writing to Sir George Denys in 1861:-

"A good quantity of a very poor quality bouse ore still continues to be wrought east from workings over the old workings of Old Rake Vein, which takes a good deal of washing and dressing up".

Bunting Level-smithy with the Sun Hush in background (YDNPA)

lease, in 1849, they undertook to drive the Low Level in Fryerfold Vein westwards from Brandy Bottle until it connected with Bunting Level. This was done by 1855 and it opened a phase of prospecting and working in the Underset Limestone and Underset Chert from Bunting Level. Around 1849 Jock Crosscut was driven southwards from a point on the Old Rake where Bunting Level was below the Underset Limestone. It found Watersikes Vein around 1855 after a drive of 2100 feet. The vein was followed for a considerable distance, despite its being very poor:-

"Watersikes Vein [March 1861] - this place has within the last fortnight rather improved in the Underset Chert and Lime Beds, but there is still no ore in the Upper Bearing Beds".

In November 1862, some *"60 men and boys"* were described as *"following up 'Old Men's' workings"*. A rich oreshoot was cut in 1866, however, and this was worked until the early 1870s.

The dressing floor at Bunting Level was probably refurbished in the mid-1850s to cope with ore from workings on Fryerfold Vein. Mechanised roller crushers made it much easier and cheaper to dress poor quality ore, which was disseminated amongst the gangue minerals. Such ore was left unworked

Mechanised hotching tubs also reduced the cost of treating the crushed ore, but their inclusion as part of a 'new dressing process' at Sir Francis Level in 1880 suggests that they were not used at Bunting Level. Some idea of dressing costs in the mid-1860s is given in the table below. This shows that normal ore was dressed for four shillings per bing, with higher rates for poorer ores.

Bouse ore washing at the Old Gang Mine

	Bings	Cwt	Rate	£	s	d
Bunting	2	1	3/-	0	6	4
	61	3	5/-	15	6	11
Hard Level	169	0	4/-	33	16	0
Hard Level & Forefield	8	1	4/-	1	12	6

In the 1880s, a crosscut from Fryerfold Shaft developed Rigg Vein on the north side of Fryerfold Vein. It was stoped in the Main Chert and the Main Limestone, where a cavern was discovered. Ore was also being raised from Rigg String in the Main Chert, Black and Red Beds in early 1884.

All the Old Gang mines were abandoned in December 1887 when the stables and offices at Bunting Level had *"recently undergone repairs and all is in good repair"*. The mine was put on care and maintenance, with a few men dressing and smelting the remaining ore

Miller's Crosscut (M. Roe)

three feet wide, but it was very hard and had little ore, so it was abandoned in December 1898.

A little way to the south of Bunting Level was Watersikes Level. This was driven in the Black Beds to try the western end of Watersikes Vein which, when it was cut in July 1820, was described as being unworked. The vein was barren, however, and the level was driven through Morey Vein to the Old Rake, but little work was done and it was idle in 1824. In 1852, the vein was tried in the Main Limestone from a short hand level, about 450 feet to the north-west.

The mouth of Sir George Level, which began near the side of the beck below Bunting Level, has been buried by a landslip. The beck has also eroded parts of the dressing floor and bouse teams. Jaques & Company began the level soon after they leased the mine in 1828, but gave up in June 1833. Sir George Level was driven near the base of the 27 Fathom Grit, about 120 feet deeper than Bunting Level, and after 670 feet it cut the combined Old Rake – Fryerfold Vein. The vein was poor, but the level was well placed to try it in the Grit and the Third Limestone, which is about 18 feet thick.

Messrs Jaques reopened Sir George Level in 1864 and raised a little ore from it. The vein was followed west to the beck, and east for 1560 feet, where the Old Rake was

and completing arching in the levels.

When the Old Gang Lead Mining Company Ltd took over in January 1889, it immediately reopened Bunting Level where it began raising ore in Old Rake Sun Vein in the Main Limestone, and in Rigg String in the Underset Lime. By February 1890, the new company was raising ore in Rigg String, Rigg Vein, Bunting Sun Vein and Watersikes Vein, in the Red Beds west of Jock's Crosscut. Output from Bunting Level was falling by the mid-1890s, when a durk drift was driven east in Rigg String in the Main Limestone. The string was from two to

Bouse teams at Sir George Level (YDNPA)

explored. Sir George Level was also linked to Bunting Level by a rise in the Old Rake. The bouse teams and small dressing floor at Sir George probably also belong to this period, but if a waterwheel-powered roller crusher was used, all traces of it have been eroded by the beck.

Total of Bouse Ore for September 1864

	Tons
Hard Level	25.90
Forefield	13.15
Brandy Bottle	2.60
Kinning	3.80
Barbara	0.45
Bunting	15.45
Sir George Level	11.45
	72.80

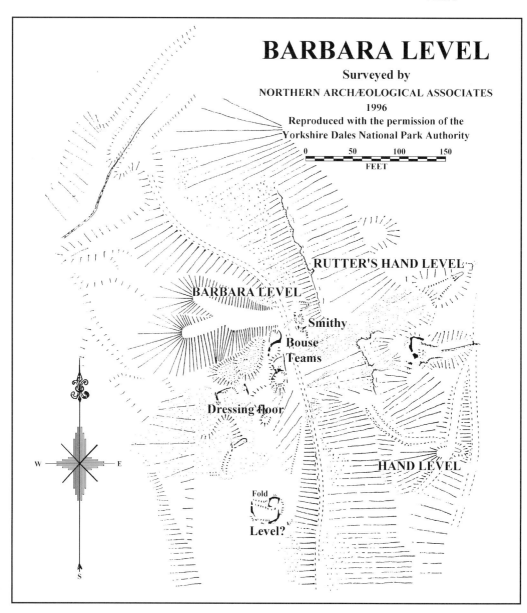

BARBARA LEVEL

Surveyed by

NORTHERN ARCHÆOLOGICAL ASSOCIATES

1996

Reproduced with the permission of the Yorkshire Dales National Park Authority

0   50   100   150

FEET

RUTTER'S HAND LEVEL

BARBARA LEVEL

Smithy

Bouse Teams

Dressing floor

HAND LEVEL

Fold

Level?

Three levels have been driven in the area where Barbara (Barbary) Vein outcrops in the Main Limestone on the east side of Gunnerside Gill. Apart from spoil heaps, however, the remains are slight.

The main workings were from Barbara Level, which begins in the bed of grit under the Main Limestone, and has a large spoil heap. At this point, however, the vein was barren and by 1824 the level was abandoned and the rails had been taken out. It was reopened around 1857 and a branch level was driven from the old crosscut. By November 1862, the forehead was about 2400 feet south-east of the level mouth, and some *"30 men and boys* [were] *working over the 'Old Men's' places"*. About 120 feet back from the forehead was a rise to Kinning Level, about 180 feet above.

At the top of the slope, behind Barbara Level, is a short cutting leading to a level. This is Rutter's Hand Level, named after Ralph Rutter who, with two partners, began driving it in the autumn of 1890 to try the vein in the Main Chert. They had cut the vein by early 1891 and followed it for about 50 feet south-east, with Black Beds on the north side and chert on the south side. A small oreshoot was expected to *"pay at 30 shillings per bing"*, but it was soon cut out by *'Old Man'* workings from a shaft. In July 1894 two men began sinking from Rutter's Level to prove the vein in the Main Limestone. A rise found some ore at the top Black Beds and in the Red Beds, but it proved to be insufficient to pay costs and the trial was abandoned by April 1896.

In the spring of 1895, a short hand level was begun, 230 feet south-east of Barbara Level, to prove an unworked string in the Main Limestone.

Scar Level can be seen in the enclosed lands on the east side of Gunnerside Gill. It was in ground leased from the Lord of the Manor by the Old Gang Company and according to Fawcett, *"In the gill at the north end of the limestone scar immediately above the village* [Gunnerside] *a level named Scar Level was driven by Pratt & Ptrs in a strong east and west vein for about 100 fathoms"*.

The prominent tips from Kinning Level can be seen on the hill shoulder, high above Gunnerside. It was started by Messrs Jaques in the early 1840s and followed Kinning Vein north-west in the Main Limestone to its junction with Barbara Vein, which was reached around 1855. The level had its own dressing floors, but was never a large producer of ore and only six men worked there in November 1862.

MINES ON BARNEY BECK

Barney, or Barnop, Beck flows into the Swale a little upstream of Healaugh and its upper reaches cut across the most important veins in Swaledale. Above its junction with Bleaberry (Billberry) Beck the valley is usually known as Mill Gill as far as Ashpot Gill, where it becomes Level Gill as far as Level House. Then it becomes Flincher (Flint Chert) Gill. It should not be supposed that the section called Level Gill draws its name from Hard Level, however, as it was called this long before the latter was driven. The level, after which it and Level House are named, was driven in the late 17th century onto the Old Rake.

Although mining in the manor of Healaugh has a much longer history, the first known lease of the mines there was to Leonard Close, of Blades, on December 30th 1561. The early miners were generally granted a few meers on the vein of their choice and allowed to work in return for paying a duty (often 1/5th) on all the ore raised. The rights of such miners were protected in a lease between Philip Lord Wharton, as mineral lord, and Philip Swale, of Hartforth, and Robert Barker, of Chesterfield, dated February 27th 1669. The lessees, who took Lord Wharton as a partner, undertook to pay a rent of 20 shillings per fother (22 cwt) of lead ore raised at Healaugh. Their mines were at Fryerfold and Merryfield, and they sank a shaft in Bleaberry Gill, near the boundary with Arkengarthdale.

In 1679, they were negotiating the terms of a new lease, and Lord Wharton wanted a higher rate of duty, but Barker and Swale argued that:-

"by that time we have worked out our old works, the trials will be harder and more discouraging than they was at first, we finding the works to be uncertain, the vein of all we know of at present lying deep, shafts hard to get, chopwood spent, price of lead very low etc."

They finally settled on 22 shillings per fother of lead ore raised at Healaugh. Lord Wharton also took a larger share of the partnership, which was divided as follows:-

Lord Wharton	7/12
Robert Barker	4/12
Philip Swale	1/12

Four-fifths of Robert Barker's one-third share were held by him on behalf of eight partners from Derbyshire. When he died, in 1681, his share was divided equally amongst his four daughters, and his brother, Adam, took over the management of the mines.

Swale and Barker undertook to build a smelt mill when their mines produced enough ore, but they smelted at the following mills in Lower Swaledale between 1671 and 1674:-

Mill	Owner
Gilling	Humphrey Wharton
Clints	Charles Bathurst
Marrick	Marquis of Winchester
Capt. Ro[binson]	Jerome Robinson

Robinson's mill was in Whashton, and Sir Thomas Wharton bought it when Robinson died in April 1675.

The partners had a mill on Barney Beck by August 1674, when Lord Wharton gave instructions *"that there be a tally kept at Swaledale Mill as the rest"*, but we do not know if it was the High Mill or the Low Mill at Surrender. Whichever it was, a second mill was built by December 1682. A slag mill, later called the New Mill, was also built at Surrender during 1685. Despite having their own mills, the partners smelted ore at Sir

Thomas Wharton's, Ellerton, Waitwith and (West) Burton smelt mills in 1683 and 1684.

In the first half of 1684, some 20 miners and 24 waste workers raised 305-tons of ore. Of this, 113-tons were smelted at Sir Thomas Wharton's smelt mills in Whashton and Gilling, whilst the other 192-tons were smelted at the High and Low Hearths on Barney Beck. Together, this made 177-tons of lead.

Barker and Swale were both dead by August 1693, when James Gorton and Robert Bradbury were granted *"ye old ground from Burnt Cove Shaft to Lownathwaite Beck"* and *"ye old Gange Rake from Level House to Lownathwaite Beck"*. It was probably this James Gorton who gave his name to Gorton Rake on the east side of Gunnerside Gill. This is the first known reference to Old Gang and it was clearly being applied to the Old Rake, rather than the whole area, as is done now.

Thomas, Fifth Lord Wharton had miners at Fryerfold and Lownathwaite in 1705, and when he died in 1715 they were working at:-

Fryerfold	Kisdon
Merryfield	Glovergill
Old Rake	Spout Gill
Keld Pasture	

There is a break in records until 1735, when the mines were in the hands of the Duke of Wharton's Trustees, whose principal mines were those now regarded as the Old Gang. This name is never used in the accounts, however, which always describe them as *"the Lead Mines in Swaledale in the possession of the Trustees of the late Duke of Wharton"*. The mines were in three groups, at Swinnergill, Lownathwaite and Merryfield.

In June 1735, the London Lead Company wanted to lease ground on the Old Rake and Merryfield Vein between Gunnerside Gill and Barney Beck, with 100 yards north and south of the veins. It also wanted all the ground from 100 yards south of Freeman's Vein to the river, and was willing to allow any persons already in possession of mining bargains to continue working them under the same terms, provided that they worked no lower than the

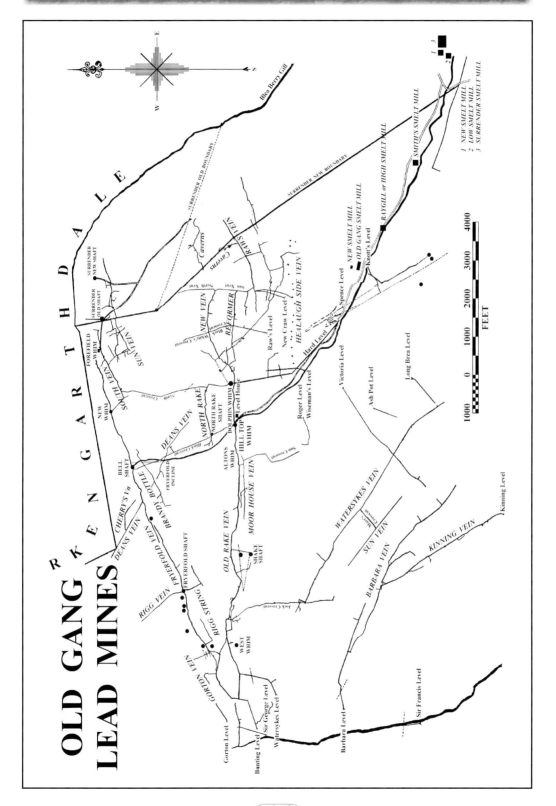

OLD GANG LEAD MINES

prevailing water table. Nothing came of their proposal, however.

By the 1740s, some miners were directly employed by the trustees, whilst others contracted either to work a number of meers, or to undertake a specific task. This system was maintained when the Earl of Pomfret took over the mines. At first glance this looks like a form of the Customary Mining Law used at the Marrick Mines during the monastic period, but it was not. Each meer was 30 yards long and, whilst not usually given, the quarter-cord was probably $7\frac{1}{2}$ yards on either side of the vein, though wider ones, of 10 or 15 yards, are noted. The following is a typical bargain from the period 1739 to 1772:-

> *"OLD RAKE - May 31st 1756. Then granted and let to Anthony Milner (Woodcock) & ptrs 2 meers of ground at an old shaft last wrought by Samuel Moore, and they are to have 30 shillings per bing for the first 50 bings, and 25 shillings per bing for all the ore they get afterwards in the said meers and the working thereof to be subject to the custom of the field, and the directions of the agent, and no part or share of the bargain is to be sold or transferred without licence from the chief agent on pain of forfeiting the same."*

The miners, who were tightly regulated under this system, worked as partners and no doubt shared costs and profits in ratio to pre-agreed shares in the venture, but could only trade those shares with the written consent of the Chief Agent. The rate received for their ore was fixed, except that (as above) the initial output was often paid for at an enhanced rate to cover the cost of opening the mine. Sometimes, the miners were paid for specific dead work, intended to prove new ground or to drain or ventilate existing workings. In some cases a partnership was restricted to the Top Set (Main) Limestone, whilst another partnership was allowed to work the Underset Limestone in the same meers. The bargains allow us to identify the head of each partnership, but rarely give the names or numbers of partners. A few, like the one above, give nick-names, which were common in Swaledale, and some give immediate family relationships. For example, *"to give William Spensley & ptrs an old bargain last wrought by Robert Spensley (his brother) & ptrs"*.

On average, the Trustees' Mines produced 638 tons of ore every six months between June 1750 and May 1756. By far the largest part of this came from Fryerfold and Old Rake Veins, with contributions from Freeman Rake, Merryfield, Hazel Kell, Lownathwaite and Swinnergill.

Most of the mining was still being done from shafts, but sometimes the option was given for using hushing if a vein was considered to be worked out. Obviously, hushing could not be used where miners were still working underground! At the eastern end of the field, near Level Beck, Adam Bird and partners were granted two areas in which to hush. The first, in June 1767, was for:-

> *"all the ground from George Reynoldson's ground east to Level Beck, being 300 yards in length and they are to have 40 yards side ground on each side of the vein ... They are to work ... the Old Vein by hushing, or in the mineral way if they find it necessary".*

In March 1769, the same partners took *"8 meers of ground in every vein, string, flot or pipe they can discover by hushing on a platt of ground called Roger"*. This was an area to the south of Old Rake, where Roger Level was later driven. Adam Bird also gave his name to a hush on Martin's Vein, in Arkengarthdale.

Some hushes, like the one on Old Rake east from Level Beck, are much older, because Level House, which stands in this hush, is mentioned in a 1693 lease. Level House was substantially rebuilt in 1777, and the level, from which the house and the beck took their names, was driven west on Old Rake in the late 17th century. It was too small to be used for haulage, but acted as a drain for workings in the Crow Limestone and Chert, which were important to the early miners. The level was used into the 1750s:-

"Ralph Fothergill for keeping in good and sufficient repair all the shafts, sumps and other waygates belonging Old Rake Level from the said 1st day of June to 1st day of December 1750 = £7 7s 0d."

The Duke of Wharton's Trustees ran the mines until George Fermor, 2nd Earl of Pomfret, married Anna-Maria Draycott in 1764. She inherited the remaining Wharton estates, but a settlement, dated May 1st 1764, gave Fermor control of one-half of the mines, whilst his wife retained the other half. At first, this change made little obvious difference and the mines continued with Jeremiah Hutchinson as Steward. In February 1770, however, Lord Pomfret appointed John Metcalfe, a miner of Dykeheads, as his Chief Steward of the lead mines in Swaledale. It was Metcalfe's job to oversee the other agents, ensure that bargains were let fairly, that lead was smelted and sent to market and that the accounts properly kept. Lord Pomfret sacked Metcalfe in October 1774, claiming that he *"had acted in a very injurious and fraudulent manner by letting bargains unknown to him"*. Moreover, because Lord Pomfret refused to pay the miners, workmen and others employed by him, Metcalfe was thrown into debt and was declared bankrupt. This meant that until he died, on June 6th 1785, individual miners were obliged to bring successful actions at law against Lord Pomfret for recovery of their dues.

Metcalfe's replacement was William Brown, of Heaning in Bishopdale. He was appointed in November 1774, but problems soon arose over 10 meers of ground at Merryfield, which he granted to *"Mr James Hawkswell, Reverend Mr John Langhorn, Thomas Dennison, Simon Peacock, George Harker and Robert Sunter Jnr"*.

The ground had been tried before without success, but they found a vein and applied to John Harker, Lord Pomfret's field agent, to have their 10 Meers set out. This was done and the partners continued raising ore and

Level House (YDNPA)

also sank a large whim shaft, at a cost of over £200. In December 1776, however, the Earl of Pomfret and William Brown evicted them and worked the mine directly, raising some 500 fothers.

The outcome of this case is not known, but yet another Chief Steward, called Alderson, was in place by December 1777. It was also around this time that the owners began to take direct control of the mines, marking the start of a shift from the 18th mode of working, with its myriad shafts, to the more centralised approach of the 19th century. New, deep Gin Shafts were sunk and railways were used underground for the first time, but, more importantly, a new level was begun from a point in Level Gill in the summer of 1777. Intended to cut the Old Rake near Level House, at first it was called Force Level, but the name was changed to Hard Level when the Underset and Main Limestones dipped into the level and slowed the rate of progress. It is not known when Hard Level reached the vein, but it was probably in 1790 when output began to rise sharply. This led to a new smelt mill being built, which began smelting in late January 1797 (see below).

When the Earl of Pomfret died, in June 1785, his estates were managed by Anna-Maria, Countess Dowager of Pomfret, and John Perrott, who established rules for running the mines and put them on a sound footing. They also acted as guardians for his children, who were all minors. They were Lady Charlotte Fermor (19) who was to have half a share in the mine, and George, 3rd Earl

**Hard Level
(YDNPA)**

of Pomfret, (18) and the Honourable Thomas William Fermor (15), who both had a quarter share.

Lady Charlotte Fermor married Peter Denys, a dancing master, in August 1787, and her brothers, George 3rd Earl of Pomfret and Thomas William Fermor, were 21 in January 1789 and November 1791 respectively. Peter Denys' background may seem an odd one for running lead mines in the Yorkshire Dales, but he was to be important in forming policy in the early 19th century.

The mineral lords sought to reduce their financial involvement in the mines by leasing them to groups of entrepreneurs from the late 18th century onwards. They seldom withdrew entirely, however, and the second Sir George Denys was very active in promoting mining interests in the area.

The early miners concentrated on the veins associated with Fryerfold and Old Rakes, which run from Barney Beck to Gunnerside Gill. Nevertheless, veins were known to cross Hall and Brownsey Moors, south of the Old Rake, but little was done on them until Barbara and Watersikes Levels were driven

from Gunnerside Gill. Ore was being raised at Barbara by July 1802 and Watersikes Level was begun around 1818 and in July 1820 John Davies reported that it had cut a vein. This area became increasingly important as the other veins were worked out, but, though some good finds were made, it never equalled the older veins.

The ground drained by the Hard and Bunting Levels was very rich throughout the 1790s and the first ten years of the 19th century. It must, however, have been clear that major expenditure would soon be needed to keep them productive. Although Hard Level began immediately below the Underset Limestone, when it reached the Old Rake the dip of the beds had taken most of the Main Limestone below the level, thus depriving the miners of access to the principal sources of ore. In March 1806, therefore, Peter Denys and John Davies discussed sinking a large diameter shaft near Level House, at a place called Peter Jarney. This was to meet the North Rake Vein workings and also to try both Merryfield and the Old Rake to the westwards in the Underset Beds.

They had also considered a scheme for developing the eastern end of the Fryerfold Vein, in the Forefield area. This would have involved sinking Reynoldson's Shaft to the Underset Limestone and building a 10 horse power steam engine to draw the work to the surface and pump the water to the natural fissure, which drained the water from the workings.

The estimated cost for the above projects was around £1800 and, faced with this expenditure, the AD Lessors decided to let the Old Gang Mine to a company. On July 31st 1811, therefore, it was leased to two brothers, Sir George and Thomas Alderson, both lead merchants and pewterers of London, for 21 years. They and their father had been born in London, but their grandfather was born at Sleightholme in the parish of Bowes in North Yorkshire.

In addition to paying a duty of 1/5th of all the lead produced, the Aldersons also agreed to pay a rent of £2163, in advance, on July 1st every year. The rate of duty was fairly typical, but the rent, which reflected the then high price of lead, was to prove disastrous. Covenants in the lease stipulated that all levels and shafts would be walled and arched with stone, and that at least 24 miners would be employed on the following dead work:-

1. To drive Force, or Hard, Level until it cut Fryerfold Vein.
2. To drive Draw Well Level (a branch of Hard Level) west as far as Merryfield smithy.
3. To drive Bunting Level east as far as Merryfield smithy.
4. To drive Barras End Level up to the Surrender boundary.

At first, the Aldersons employed John Davies, who was also the lessors' agent, to manage their mines. He might have been a sound practical miner, but he does not seem to have been up to running such a large mine. With the exception of driving Barras End Level there is little to suggest that he did much towards fulfilling the above objectives. Output fell quickly and in June 1813 Davies reported that the workings were very poor. A branch of Hard Level was being driven east on Level House Vein, but it was hard and poor. They were also driving on Lucky String towards Surrender, but were again being troubled by the '*Old Man*'.

Faced with Davies's failure to raise more ore, the Aldersons employed Frederick Hall to run their mine from May 1814. Hall was also managing the Arkindale & Derwent Mines Company's mines in Arkengarthdale and around Blanchland in Northumberland. In both places he had undertaken grandiose and expensive schemes to open up the fields, sinking new shafts, installing steam engines, driving new levels and building new smelt mills.

One of Frederick Hall's first acts was to sack Davies, whose reports to the AD Lessors display one side of the animosity between them. Hall stopped driving Barras End Level in July 1814 and in December he stopped the

Hard Level (YDNPA)

forehead of Bunting Level, both acts being contrary to the covenants of the lease. He concentrated work on developing the Brandy Bottle and Forefield areas, at the head of Flincher Gill, and the North Rake, near Level House.

In early June 1814 he began driving Black Crosscut from a point near North Rake Whim which was 24 feet above Hard Level. This was done to take advantage of the easier driving offered by the bed of plate on top of the Underset Chert. Davies and others later criticised Hall for losing this 24 feet of depth, but he had realised that the productive beds near Bell's Shaft, where the crosscut reached Fryerfold Vein, were all either at or above the Main Level, or much more than 24 feet below it. There was, therefore, little point in driving in the much harder Underset beds, which would have been both slower and much more expensive. As it was, the crosscut took two years to complete.

Davies's reports to Peter Denys, fill in many details. In April 1814, for example, he wrote that:-

"The two large waterwheels is expected to be up in the course of six weeks time and fixed a little west of the mill's peat house, and an incline plane are now preparing from Brandy Bottle down to the waterwheels. About 30 tons of cast iron rails is arrived and a vast [deal] *more to come".*

This reference to waterwheels is ambiguous. One may have been built on the surface, but the other may have been built underground for pumping sumps sunk into the Underset beds on the footwall of Fryerfold Vein. If so, the tail water from the latter wheel and the water it pumped may either have been led into the swallow, mentioned above as being near Reynoldson's Shaft, or sent down Black Crosscut.

Hall also took down the whims at Forefield, Alton and Reynoldson's Shafts, on which the mine had depended, and began driving the North Rake Incline from the surface near Level House. This was 400 feet long and sloped at 1 in 2, falling 27 fathoms to the Main Level, near North Rake Whim, about 24 feet above Hard Level. It was five feet high by 3 feet 9 inches between timbers, cost £905 and took 18 months to drive, but was never used.

The Fryerfold Inclined Plane, which is sometimes called the Brandy Bottle Incline, was driven from the surface on the west side of Flincher Gill. The first 455 feet were driven at 1 in 3 to the Middle Level, near the foot of Willan's Shaft, in the Brandy Bottle Vein. There was also a Top Level, driven from the point where King Gig Shaft cut the incline, to cut Fryerfold Vein where the Flint Chert was on the hanging wall. The Middle Level crosscut to Fryerfold Vein found the Main Limestone on the hanging wall, opposite the Red and Black Beds. The incline then sloped at 1 in 2 for 295 feet to the Main Level, making a total fall of 276 feet. The foot of the incline was about 55 feet short of Fryerfold Vein, where the Main Limestone was on the footwall, opposite the Underset Chert and Limestone.

A small steam engine pulled two waggons, each weighing 9 cwts, with a 16 cwt load, at a time. What some writers have described as a second, unfinished incline, running alongside the main one to the Flint Chert Level, carried a weighted waggon running on rails, which acted as a counter-balance for the load on the engine when winding. The rope was put on this incline in May 1818, but the engine appears never to have worked. By May 1819 the engine had been replaced by a horse whim as an experiment in working the incline.

Peter Denys died in the early summer of 1816 and his affairs were run by William Richards, his agent in London. There had been some discussion about the value of Alton Whim Shaft which, as it was sunk in the vein, the Aldersons claimed was expensive to keep open and useless. They proposed extending Old Rake Hush over the shaft, having removed the rails and pipes about two years earlier, as the best means of getting any remaining ore. By March the following year, Hall had begun hushing and Richards asked that work be suspended to give him

Fryerfold Incline

opportunity to find out if that method of working was appropriate. Hall responded that Alton's Shaft was safe and that the hush, which was not a new one, had also been worked by Davies!

Hall's schemes failed to raise output significantly and, in July 1818, he was sacked after claiming that he should have been paid ten per cent of the value of the lead raised,

Waggon wheels near foot of Fryerfold Incline

without deduction for dead work. The Aldersons insisted that the agreement was that he would get ten per cent of the profits, after deducting the cost of dead work. Hall's claim for damages amounted to £60,000 and so the matter went to law. In June 1819 the matter was referred to arbitration, but the outcome is not known.

The remaining years of the Alderson lease were little better than the earlier ones, with rapidly varying fortunes. Output from the Old Gang Mine increased a little, but the AD Lessors began demanding that they comply with the covenants of their lease. Driving was resumed at Barras End Level in late September 1820, but the men were only *"able to drive one yard a week* [because] *it is very hard, but in 30 or 40 fathoms will cut a vein - but the airway is run"*.

Dilapidation surveys, made in July 1824 and July 1826, show that around £4800 of work was needed to put the mines in order. Barras End Level had been standing since August 1823 and the airway was incomplete and part of it had been driven above the level's roof, as opposed to its side which was considered proper. The North Rake Whim Shaft had fallen in, making the whole of the works on that vein useless until it was repaired. To open out and wall the shaft would cost five pounds per fathom or £175 for 35 fathoms. Many other levels and shafts were described as *"standing upon wood"* and needed arching with stone. New Whim Shaft, which had been sunk on Fryerfold Vein in lieu of Reynoldson's Shaft, fell into the latter category and would cost £175 to line the 25 fathoms needed. The Fryerfold Incline was still open, but was only used for access. Alton Whim Shaft and Airway Shaft, both on Old Rake, were run in and closed. The hushing, which was discussed in 1816, had obviously gone ahead because the shaft and much of its hillock had been washed away.

Many of the leading figures changed around this time. John Davies died, aged 67 years, and was buried at Grinton Church on November 26th 1822. His successor, James Littlefair, deputised at first and was appointed as agent for the AD Lessors in June 1824. Sir George Alderson died in 1826 and his brother, Thomas, was left in charge of the mines. His failure to act on the dilapidations led to a law suit with the lessors, in which the latter won damages of £2257 3s 0d.

The following new company took over from Thomas Alderson on August 13th 1828.

Robert Jaques	Easby
Matthew Whitelock	Cogden Hall
George Robinson	Richmond
Ottiwell Tomlin	Richmond
Edmund Alderson Knowles	Low Row

These men and their successors were to dominate the lead industry in Swaledale and Arkengarthdale until the 1870s, when the area's mines went into crisis. For example, Jaques, Knowles and Tomlin were also involved at Hurst, Arkengarthdale and Fremington.

This new venture must also have seemed doomed to failure because, almost immediately, the price of lead began to fall from an average of £17 0s 0d per ton in 1828 to £12 5s 0d in 1830 and £11 13s 0d in 1832 before recovering. Nevertheless, despite a fall in output during 1830, the company was able to increase its output steadily and, from 1832, got it back to almost 1000 tons of metallic lead. First, however, the new company had to rectify the problems left by Messrs Alderson and so it began walling and arching the levels. Between February 1829 and September 1830 it was paid £927 10s 0d for doing 1325 fathoms of this work by the lessors. Unfortunately there are few records of developments in this period, but the link between Bunting and Hard Levels, on Old Rake, was made in 1828.

When the lease was renewed in 1839, the company undertook to drive Bunting Level east on Fryerfold Vein from Miller's Crosscut, and to drive the Low Level west from the foot of the Fryerfold Incline to meet it. By April 1848 Bunting Level was approaching Raws Shaft, near Turnpike End, and the level from the incline had been driven beyond it in what appears to be a near parallel branch of Fryerfold Vein. There is no indication of a direct connection, although they were very close. The company was also to extend the horizontal chimney by 1800 feet and direct all the smoke from the various furnaces into it. Whilst not mentioned in the lease, it is likely that the Old Gang Smelt Mill was built in 1845 and began smelting early in the following year.

The 1840s and 1850s were a time of exploration. Pedley's, or North, Crosscut, at the horizon of Hard Level, was driven towards the Forefield area on Fryerfold Vein in the 1850s. It stopped at Forefield Old Sun Vein, which had been worked from Reynoldson's and Forefield Whim Shafts on Fryerfold Vein.

The veins under Healaugh Crag, towards the boundary with the Surrender Mine, were also tried at this time. Many years before, Healaugh Side Vein was tried from shafts and from a branch of Hard Level. Hazel Keld Vein, which runs southwards from Garth Fold and outcrops in the Underset beds near Hard Level, had been tried by shafts and by hushing in the late 18th century. Spence Level was

Spence Level with Hazel Keld Hush behind (YDNPA)

driven onto it soon afterwards and was used as a water supply for the smelt mills from 1805. The level was reopened in 1876, when it was said to be promising in the Underset Beds, but nothing came of it. Wiseman's Level, which probably dates from the same period, had been driven to Healaugh Side Vein, but Jaques & Company undertook both to enlarge it and drive it to Raw's Vein. In November 1854 they were driving a durk drift south, in the Main Limestone, to Spensley's Folly.

Two levels, Raw's (or Old Craw Beds) and New Craw, were driven to try Reformer and Raw's Veins in the Crow Beds which were almost the highest strata likely to carry ore. They also tried a vein called Hazel Keld, which runs parallel to the vein of the same name (see above), but may be an extension of Dean's Vein. These same veins, plus Lucky String and New Vein, were also followed eastwards from Hard Level, which was probably near the base of the Main Limestone as it went under Crag Willas. A number of crosscuts, driven north and south from New Vein, found little that was new, but proved Reformer and Raw's Veins. Whilst Raw's Vein was being driven east, an extensive series of natural caverns was discovered in the Main Limestone. Caverns were found elsewhere in the Old Gang Mines, but this one appears to rival those seen in Arkengarthdale and at Grinton. This part of the mine appears to have been largely worked out by the mid-1860s and only one trial of the Undersets in recorded, via a sump on New Vein.

After the failures of Watersikes and Barbara Levels in the 1820s, the veins in the area south of Old Rake, on Hall and Brownsey Moors, were developed by driving Kinning Level, reopening Barbara and by driving Jock's Crosscut from Bunting Level.

In order to work the south-east end of Watersikes Vein, Victoria Level was begun from Ashpot Gutter in 1858. Unfortunately, it was driven too steeply and, after being abandoned for a while, its sole was taken up to get lower in the bearing bed. By the mid-1860s, the level had cut Watersikes Vein and its Sun Vein. They were very productive and,

in 1875, Sir George Denys complained that the Old Gang Company had neglected other parts of the mine while Watersikes was rich.

1857	Tons of ore
Barrass	21.60
Hard Level	571.90
Forefield	123.30
Kinning	992.50
Bunting	518.90
	2228.20

Other trials were made in that area, however, and in May 1854 Roger Level, named after the area in which it was driven, tried Healaugh Side Vein at the top of the Main Lime on the west side of Level Gill and found it barren. Ashpot Level was being driven towards Watersikes Vein in September 1855, to try it in the beds above the Main Limestone. It was mostly used as a waygate after it was linked to Victoria Level.

When Hazel Keld Vein crosses Level Gill Beck, it becomes Knotts Vein, which has been tried from two levels. The Low Level was driven from near the side of the beck in 1857 and followed the vein south with a little success. A hand level, called Knotts High Level, was begun nearby in 1862 and cut Knotts Vein by the end of the year. Little work was done on it, however, and by the following August the level had cut a parallel vein. Although they never amounted to much, the company persisted with these trials and, in August 1868, James Alderson was drawing the work at Knotts and other levels, whilst in March 1872 a hand level was being driven in Knotts Vein. The trials appear to have been abandoned soon afterwards.

With output from Watersikes Vein about to fall off, Long Brea, or Bob, Level was begun in May 1871 to look for the vein's southern continuation. The level was in the plate and limestone, between the Main Chert and the Black Beds, and six men were reported to have driven nearly 85 fathoms in 12 weeks, which is 42 feet per week. Although nothing by modern standards, this was an incredible rate of advance then. Sadly, Watersikes Vein loses its strength and was not worked.

Hopes then turned to some weak veins which run roughly east to west across Brownsey Moor. The southernmost of these was Scarr's Vein, which was also tried by a level near the mouth of Gunnerside Gill. In 1862, the AD Lessors had wanted the company to begin a new level to explore Pot Ing (Potting) Vein. This was probably what became Dunn's or Barf Head Level, which Thomas Bewick described as unpromising in August 1871. It began about 300 feet north of Barf End Farm and cut Scarr's Vein, which it followed west for a short distance to Kinning Vein. This was followed north-west, looking for Dunn's Vein, which it did not reach before being abandoned in September 1872.

Around the same time, Brownsey Level was begun from 500 feet north-west of Brownsey House. It was driven north and cut Dunn's Vein, which was poor, and continued in search of the southern end of Watersikes Vein. It was abandoned, without finding it, at the end of 1871 after being driven 430 feet.

The end was in sight for the Old Gang Mine, although it proved to be some way off. Production fell quickly in the mid-1870s, from 1687 tons of metal in 1874 to 691 tons in 1877. J.R. Tomlin, one of the directors, wrote to Sir George Denys in August 1879, pointing out that *"the Old Gang Mining Company had lost a considerable sum of money during the last three or four years in working these mines"*. He asked for the covenant requiring them to employ 24 men on dead work to be suspended, but Sir George refused as it would have meant the end for Sir Francis Level.

The Old Gang Company had one brief success during these years, when it drove a level onto Fryer Intake Vein, which was leased from the Lord of the Manor because it was in the old enclosures. This vein, which runs nearly north to south, midway between Smarber and Jenkin House, had been tried from shafts around 1740.

George Calvert and three partners undertook to drive a 50 fathom long crosscut to Fryer Intake Vein in March 1871 and to complete it in four months. The site chosen was at the foot of Fryer Intake, near the B6270 road, which runs up Swaledale. The 1854 OS map shows an old level, about which nothing is known, in almost the same place. By December 1876 from 50 to 60 bings of ore per month were being raised from the Fifth Limestone, but this did not last, because that bed is very thin, and the mine closed soon afterwards.

For the next ten years, with the exception of Sir Francis Level, work concentrated on getting ore in old parts of the mine from Bunting and Hard Levels. By May 1887, Hard Level was being driven east in Forefield Sun Vein, with both sides in the Main Limestone. They had reached the Surrender boundary and the lessors had given the company permission to continue. The vein carried *"very nice pockets of ore"* which were being worked by two men. A durk drift was being driven on Deans Vein from Fryerfold Incline, and ore was raised there from the top part of the Main Lime and Chert. The vein was from four to five feet wide, and of red mineral, with *"nice pockets of ore"*. Rigg Vein was in disturbed ground, but ore was being raised from places where it was whole. Ore was also being raised in Rigg String and Fryerfold Sun Vein from Bunting Level.

The mine was nearing the end in November 1887, when the AD Lessors' agent complained that:-

"The ore getters have been very limited during the last quarter. This being applicable to the very low price they are paying per bing. We have now at different parts of the mine stoups and headings standing that would pay for working if say from 30 to 25 shillings per bing were offered".

The Old Gang directors surrendered their lease in December 1887 and, except for a few partnerships gleaning a living amongst the old works, the mines were idle until December 1888, when the Old Gang Lead Mining Company Ltd was formed. Its directors were:-

John Leonard Tomlin	London
Joseph Cradock	Stockton on Tees
Frank Huntsman	Retford
George Roper	Richmond
John Ralph Milner	Leyburn- managing director

Work began on January 2nd, when ore bargains were let to 22 men on Fryerfold Sun Vein, Deans Vein and Rigg Vein. Because the mines had been standing since the end of 1887, the men were given slightly better bargain rates to cover the cost of cleaning the waygates. For example, Victoria Level was found to be in bad repair, with many roof falls and most of the rails taken out. Owing to the purchase price of the plant not having been agreed, no dead work was done until April 1889.

Old Gang Pay Bill – September 16th 1841

Simon Cherry was optimistic about Rigg String, but it was soon found to only carry patchy pockets of ore in the Red Beds. Men also began repairing and cleaning the machinery etc in Sir Francis Level, in

preparation for the company's only major trial into virgin ground. On October 22nd the water pressure engine, which had stood since 1882, began pumping out the Engine Sump. The company had over 100 men at work by January 1890.

Early in 1891 Bride's Vein was developed from Hard Level. Some ore was got, but whilst a rise was being made in the Main Limestone a deposit of barium carbonate was found and 12 tons were raised and sold for £56 1s 3d in 1892.

Deans Vein was abandoned in the summer of 1893 and the durk drift in the Main Chert, north-east of Rigg String, was stopped at the end of 1897, when the men began sinking into the Main Limestone, *"which at times contains good fair good ore, but is irregular"*. The old workings continued to produce small amounts of ore, but mining at Bunting Level came to an end when the durk drift in Rigg String was abandoned in October 1898. Output came chiefly from the Sir Francis Mine and Old Rake Sun Vein at Hard Level. This vein was described as *"very strong being from 4 to 5 feet wide of rider intermixed with fair good ore, but it is very hard to extract"*. In the second quarter of 1899 some 67 tons of ore were raised, most of it from the Old Rake Sun Vein in the Main Lime and Chert, but this had now cut into 'Old Man's' workings.

In its first five years, to 1893, the company had raised an average of 125 tons of ore per year, but output fell along with prices and, in its final 13 years, annual output averaged 50 tons. There had also been problems in the amount of lead recovered from the ore and its quality. In April 1895, for example, it was noted that *"The company have offered the lead on hand for sale, but as yet have been unable to effect a sale."*

The company was short of money and things were getting desperate. At Hard Level, White's crosscut from Old Rake Sun Vein to Forefield Sun Vein was reopened in early 1901, and miners returned to Bunting Level to raise ore in Fryerfold Vein soon after. An injection of £650 in new capital was raised to drive Sir Francis Level, but by June 1902 £390 had been spent in driving 75 fathoms and yet more would be needed.

In June 1906, Simon Cherry reported that:-

"The Directors are in treaty with Messrs Barclay & Co. bankers [the debenture holders] about the plant with a view to buying it and then to raising more money so as to enable them to resume driving Sir Francis Horse Level north in Watersikes Vein, also to make further trials in other parts of the mine."

Things had become so bad, however, that the lessors' agent took over the mines on September 29th 1906 and, at an extraordinary general meeting held on October 26th, it was agreed that the company could not continue, owing to its debts, and should be wound up.

THE AD LESSORS WORK THE MINES

As they entered 1907 with all their mines idle, the lessors sought to encourage prospective lessees. In the meantime, they repaired buildings and kept a few men at work. In July, Simon Cherry advised them that:-

"The repairs to the buildings and the smelt mill chimney at Old Gang are progressing very well. I am pleased to say there is a quantity of soot in the mill chimney left by the old company which when cleaned out I think will cover the cost of the repairs to the chimney itself. These will exceed our original estimate as several lengths of chimney have fallen

in since the date of Sir Francis's inspection in September last."

The mine was advertised, which led to several enquiries, but nothing came of them.

In September 1907, Sir Francis gave Luther Broderick and James Pratt, both of Smarber, a two year take note to search for lead ore in a 600 foot square plot of ground near Huntpots, at the east end of Brownsey. They sank a shaft, about six fathoms deep, into the Main Limestone, in Knotts Vein, but discovered no ore. The vein contained *"a great strength of red soil and clay"*. After trying two veins, but finding no ore, the take note was not renewed when it expired.

The lessors continued working the mines with a handful of men. Sir Francis and Priscilla Levels were also cleared out and repaired to allow prospective lessees to view them. A trial at Bearpark's Rise, on Old Rake Sun Vein, west of Hard Level head, found nothing and no ore was raised in the last six months of 1911. Only two hundredweights were raised in the following six months. The miners in this period were William Buxton & partner; John Walker; Henry Calvert & partner; and Anthony Watter. By the end of 1913, William Buxton's trial at Bearpark's Rise had found a little ore, and Henry Calvert had raised 1.7 tons of waste ore at Hard Level. Buxton died suddenly on December 29th 1914 and, rather ominously, no ore was raised in the first half of 1915 *"owing to sickness the few remaining miners have been unable to work"*. No miners were employed thereafter.

After World War I, interest began to shift from lead ore to recovering barytes and, on July 1st 1924, Edward Cecil Vickers took a five year lease to work the dumps between Flincher Gill and Merryfield House, and between Old Rake and Fryerfold Vein. In the following year, Vickers formed the Swaledale Lead Mines Ltd, which was granted a 21 year lease of the Old Gang ground.

In a move which was reminiscent of the great 18th century disputes, Francis Horner Lyell, the Lord of the Manor, claimed that the barytes was his property and not that of the AD Lessors. The basis of his claim was that barytes was not one of the minerals reserved when the Duke of Wharton's trustees sold the estate. Unlike those earlier times, however, the matter was resolved by negotiation and it was agreed that, because mine roads were being used to reach the dumps, the duties arising from barytes would be split fifty-fifty. About 40 tons had been sold.

Over the winter of 1924-1925, Vickers made no attempt to work the dumps because of the weather, but his two men cleaned out and repaired Victoria Level in preparation for searching for lead ore. However, none was found. They had also reopened Barras End Level in the hope of finding witherite, but only four tons of barytes were raised. This had exhausted the company's capital and it went into voluntary liquidation by June 1926.

A small partnership, called Swaledale Mines Ltd, was granted a seven year lease of minerals in and under Reeth High and Melbecks Moor in September 1948. They had a dressing plant at the Old Gang smelt mill, and also worked the dumps on Mouldside in Arkengarthdale. They treated the dumps in the Brandy Bottle and Forefield areas, and in more recent times moved their plant further upstream and housed it in a box-van body. When these men gave up, around 1990, mining in Swaledale died.

HARD LEVEL DRESSING FLOOR

The small building on the roadside at the foot of Hazel Keld hushes, near Spence's Level, is a smith's shop. It was built by the AD Lead Mining Company Ltd in the autumn of 1875, when it was using Hard Level to develop veins near the boundary between the two mines. A quarterly way-leave of £10 was paid to the Old Gang Company for this privilege.

The Old Gang dressing floor stood in the area, along the beck side between the mouth of Hard Level and the smelt mill. A line of at least seven bouse teams was built into the

banking alongside the track. Other bouse teams, parallel to them, have been buried. A few yards east of these is the pit of a large waterwheel, which drove a roller crusher. The main dressing floor was on the terraces between the crusher and the stream. Because most of the decking, equipment, water channels etc was made of wood, very little, apart from a few tumbled stones and vague shapes, has survived. There would, however, have been hotching tubs, a range of buddles (probably not circular) and dolly tubs. An oblong feature, split into five compartments, at the downstream end of the site was probably a settlement tank used for catching the very finest particles of mud and ore before they went into the beck.

A visitor to the mine in 1857 remarked that:-

"Young women are engaged at working, at the hotching tubs, and this is a matter of regret, because the employment of women in hard out-of-door work always implies a want of social refinement, which it seems the special province of this age to correct. Boys too are sent at a very early age to labour, but we must look for a reparation of these defects in the general advance of that improvement which has taken place among miners".

He continued:-

"Nothing strikes a visitor to a lead mine more than the strict economy with which every process connected with the getting, the dressing, and the smelting of lead is conducted. From the time it is dug out of its bed, to the time that it becomes an article of commerce care is taken that not one particle shall escape either out of the pockets of the workmen or the proprietors. ... the slime is sifted and passed over 'endless cloths', till every leaden tint is taken out of it, and the native mud is separated from the native ore, and then half-a-mile down the beck, people are seen scraping among the rocks

and pools for such stray pieces of ore as the water carries away."

The endless cloth referred to was a Brunton Buddle, which had a continuous belt of heavy cloth on which very fine particles of lead ore were trapped in the nap whilst lighter material was washed away.

THE SMELT MILLS

Seven of Swaledale's principal smelt mills were on Barney Beck and six of them smelted ore from the Old Gang, Surrender and Barras End Mines. There has, however, been much confusion about their histories and locations. For example, when Dr Raistrick wrote his book on the *Lead Industry of Wensleydale and Swaledale: The Smelting Mills*, he split the four early mills between Philip Lord Wharton and his brother Sir Thomas Wharton, as follows:-

NAME OF MILL	RAISTRICK'S NAME
High or Ray Gill	Sir Thomas Wharton's High
Smith's	Philip Lord Wharton's High
Low	Philip Lord Wharton's Low
New	Sir Thomas Wharton's Low

Careful re-reading of the sources for the late 17th century has shown that he was wrong, however. There is a clear distinction between Lord Wharton's and Sir Thomas Wharton's mills in the accounts. The former are always referred to as the high and low hearths in Swaledale, whilst the latter are called Sir Thomas Wharton's high and low hearths/ mills. The accounts also make it clear that Sir Thomas's mill, which he bought from Leonard Robinson in 1675, was in the manor of Ravensworth. (Sir Thomas's mills will be dealt with later, under Whashton and Gilling.)

There were no smelt mills on Barney Beck in February 1669, when Swale and Barker leased the mines from Philip Lord Wharton. They undertook to build one, however, if the produce of the mines became great enough and Lord Wharton desired it. Dr Raistrick suggested that they did this almost

immediately but, between 1671 and 1674 at least, their ore was smelted at the following mills in lower Swaledale:-

> Gilling
> Clints
> Marrick
> Capt. Ro[binson]

This delay gave them time to develop the mines. At the end of August 1674, however, Lord Wharton gave instructions *"that there be a tally kept at Swaledale Mill as the rest"*. This meant that the first mill on Barney Beck had begun smelting, but we cannot tell whether it was the High Mill or the Low Mill at Surrender. Whichever it was, the other mill was built by December 1682. A slag mill, later called the New Mill, was also built at Surrender during 1685.

The pack horses, which carried the ore from the mines to the smelt mills in the 17th and 18th centuries, were replaced by horse drawn carts in the 19th century. At the same time, pieces of lead were carried on pack horses, two per animal, from the mills to Stockton on Tees. They, too, were replaced by carts as the road system improved.

HIGH MILL

The High, or Raygill, Mill was the highest of the late-17th century mills on Barney Beck. Its precise location is not known because the valley is strewn with flood debris and mining waste. Nevertheless, evidence given at the York assizes, during 1772, states:-

> *"Lord Pomfret's water race to his high smelt mill in Raygill from the beck to the wheel 441 yards in length and from there to the tail of the race 40 yards. From the said mill to Mr Smith's weir 100 yards. Mr Smith obliged now since the destruction of the weir to fetch the water about 40 yards further than the weir from the beck to his mill. Distance from Mr Smith's mill to Lord Pomfret's Low mills 1000 yards".*

These distances, and Richardson's 1770 map of the Manor of Healaugh, put the High Mill on the north bank of the beck, slightly downstream of Ray Gill.

In 1719, the High Mill, which had one ore-hearth, was repaired by the Chaytors, who had leased the mines from the Duke of Wharton, but it was not working by 1736, when the accounts name only the Low Mill and the New Mill, which were both at Surrender. The High Mill was working again in 1750, however, suggesting that it been renovated in the 1740s. It smelted until around 1805, when a roasting furnace was built there. This was used to roast ore for the New Mill until a similar furnace was built there in 1807 and the High Mill closed.

LOW AND NEW MILLS

Dr Raistrick correctly placed the Low and New Mills near Surrender Bridge, but the latter had nothing to do with Sir Thomas Wharton, as he suggested. Both were built by Philip Swale and Robert Barker, under their lease from Philip Lord Wharton. As noted above, the High and Low Mills were built in 1674 and 1682, but we do not know which of them was built first. The Low Mill stood near the beck and its relationship with the New Mill, which was built as a slag mill in 1685, is confirmed in a letter from John Renshaw to Lord Wharton:-

"In order to a slagg harth milne, hee hath beefore hee come away, levelled & brought the watter from Blackeberye Gill, & layed the foundation of the milne, wich watter macks greate helpe to our other milne."

The New Mill was idle between 1752 and 1754, when it may have been rebuilt, but it was working again in 1755. In the early 19th century the New and Low Mills were variously called the Old, Low or Surrender Mills, and in 1806 they were taken over by the company running Surrender Mine. At that time, the two mills had three ore-hearths between them. There was also a roasting furnace which, in 1807, was repaired by Joseph Smith and partners. In 1828, the same team took down and rebuilt the roasting furnace, and repaired the furnace chimney.

SURRENDER MILL

The New and Low Mills were replaced in 1841, after a new lease, made in 1839, stipulated that the Surrender company should build a new mill and 1500 feet of flue within two years. The site chosen was on or very near the site of the New Mill, about 100 feet north of Barney Beck. The single-storied mill was 85 feet long by 31 feet wide and had an ore lobby at either end of its north wall. Ore was fed into these lobbies via chutes leading from the platform to the rear of the mill. A building added to the mill's north-east corner housed a roasting furnace, with its own vertical chimney.

The interior of the mill was split into three bays. The central one, or bellows room, was 32 feet wide and housed a waterwheel which drove the blowing machinery. At first, the latter might have been multiple bellows, but by 1860 it was a two-cylinder blowing engine, linked to an air receiver. On either side of the bellows room were the hearth rooms, each with a door in the north wall leading to the ore lobby. Each room had two hearths, set side by side, under arched canopies. There were three ore-hearths and one slag-hearth and their flues were led, one above the other, out of the back of the mill. They combined behind the mill and continued as a single, stone arched flue which originally ended 1545 feet away at a rectangular chimney. This was the lower stack and it was sealed off for a time when the flue was extended. Another chimney, of which only a few traces remain, stood 660 feet behind the mill. Around 1866, the flue was extended to a total length of 2445 feet, where it vented from another rectangular chimney, only the base of which survives. This new section of flue is

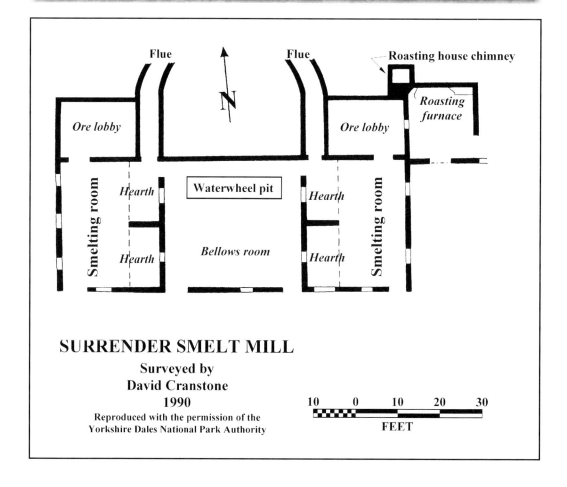

SURRENDER SMELT MILL

Surveyed by
David Cranstone
1990

Reproduced with the permission of the
Yorkshire Dales National Park Authority

10   0   10   20   30

FEET

interesting because two parts of it have been mined rather than built in the usual cut and cover fashion. Moreover, the upper of the two mined sections ends at the foot of a 40 foot deep shaft from surface. A small settling pond at the rear of the mill was for recovering lead fumes washed from the flues.

A slag crushing mill, between the mill and the beck, is thought to be on the site of the Low Mill. It had a 16 foot by 4 foot waterwheel, which drove a roller crusher.

The ruins of a peat store can be seen to the north-west of the mill. It was similar to, but smaller than, the one at the Old Gang, being 118 feet long by 15 feet wide.

The Surrender company gave up the mine in the autumn of 1873 and it was immediately taken over by the AD Lead Mining Company Ltd, of which Sir George Denys was the

managing director. In addition to the small amount of ore it raised at Surrender, the company also smelted ore from its mines at Lownathwaite and Swinnergill. This brought complaints from J.R. Tomlin, the solicitor for those with grazing rights on the moor. Tomlin, who was also a director of the Old Gang Company, claimed that it was wrong to bring in these other ores. He also complained that the fumes were killing the herbage around the high stack and demanded that the low stack, where the ground was already polluted, be brought back into use.

In September 1879, Sir George complied with this demand whilst he made enquiries about building a condenser on the flue. He even proposed building a large new smelt mill, near Gunnerside, which would smelt the ore from both the Old Gang and AD mines.

**Surrender Smelt Mill,
Peathouse and roasting
house chimney, 1946**

**Surrender Smelt Mill,
c1964**

None of this was ever done, however, and the company began to sell its ore to other smelters, after first roasting some of it at Surrender to increase its value.

Surrender Mill, which is now a Scheduled Ancient Monument, closed in 1880. Its peat house was cleared out between May and July 1882 when 162 loads of peat were taken to the Old Gang Mill. The AD Lessors continued to maintain the mill, however, and in the summer of 1882 William Pedley was paid 12 shillings for repairs. Even as late as January 1898, Thomas Brown repaired slates at the mill. In September 1902, however, the mill's roof timbers, slates, copings, doors and floor boards were sold at auction. The mill's 14 foot diameter wooden waterwheel was not sold until August 1909, when the Stang & Cleasby Lead Mines Ltd paid £50 0s 0d for it.

Aerial view of Surrender Smelt Mill and its Flue (YDNPA)

SMITH'S MILL

This mill was called Philip Lord Wharton's High Mill by Dr Raistrick, but it does not appear in accounts relating to the Wharton mines and is much more recent. Its ruins are shown as the '*site of old mill*' on early OS maps, and a track to it on the north side of the valley from Surrender Bridge, along with the remains of stonework are still visible.

When Thomas Smith bought the manors of Healaugh and Muker from the Duke of Wharton's trustees in 1738, all mines of lead, copper and iron ore in the unenclosed lands were reserved for the use of the trustees. In 1739, however, Smith claimed the minerals under an area called Beldi Hill, which he said was enclosed. He then leased Beldi Hill to John and Thomas Parke and Leonard Hartley in 1742. They smelted at the Spout Gill Mill and, around 1757, Smith also claimed this as part of his purchase.

Possibly in readiness for Lord Pomfret's trying to get Spout Gill Mill back, which he did in 1769, Smith built a new mill on Barney Beck. On various occasions between 1769 and 1771, this mill's weir and watercourse were destroyed by Lord Pomfret's men, twelve of whom were imprisoned overnight at Richmond. Because most of its ore came from Beldi Hill, which had its own mill, Smith's mill closed soon afterwards and the agent for his estate was scavenging slate and wood from it in 1784.

NEW MILL

Until it was uncovered in 1975, the New Mill (No.13), which stands in the complex of buildings behind the Old Gang Mill, had been overlooked. It began work in late January 1797, having been built to smelt part of the increased output from the Old Rake, which had been drained by Hard Level.

The New Mill had two ore-hearths, with arched canopies, which an archæological survey, made for the Yorkshire Dales National Park Authority, suggested vented into a central chimney directly over them. Nevertheless, there are records of a flue being extended by 109 yards in 1805, by 60 yards in 1806, and by 600 yards around 1829. In other words, a large part of the Old Gang smelt mill's flue, which ran to a chimney on Healaugh Crag, was built for the New Mill.

In the first six months of 1802 the mill produced some 6600 pieces of lead, weighing 458.63 tons. This meant that each piece weighed about 155 lbs and, for ready

New Smelt Mill (YDNPA)

New Smelt mill – arches for the ore-hearths (YDNPA)

OLD GANG MILL

Interestingly, whilst the Old Gang Mill was one of the largest in the area, a search of the archives has failed to reveal when it was built. Nevertheless, there are some clues. For example, the mill is shown on the first edition of the 0S 1/10560 sheet for the area, which was surveyed in 1854. Moreover, because the Old Gang Mill's flues are led into the old flue via the New Mill, the Old Gang Mill could be built without interrupting smelting. The New Mill would, however, have had to stop working when the connection was made and any openings were sealed up. The only detectable break in smelting was between February and April in 1846 which, in the absence of evidence to the contrary, is the date proposed for the transfer of smelting to the Old Gang Mill. Some idea of this mill's complexity is given by the site plan and the following description of the various buildings and their possible uses.

reckoning purposes, that 16 pieces weighed one Stockton fother, which was 22 cwts. The fuel used was peat, wood and some coal, which came from Tan Hill, William Gill and Bishopsbridge.

There are regular items in the accounts for improvements to facilities at the mill. In 1805, for example, a cinder oven, for making coke, was built. The mill's peat stack was also thatched with 180 threaves (one of which equals two dozen sheaves) of ling. Its water supply was also enhanced when Christopher Heslop was paid for *"opening the level mouth to bring water to the New Mill"*. Soon afterwards a dam door was made and fixed in the level mouth. This probably refers to Spence Level, which has a small stone culvert running from its entrance into an adjacent reservoir. It was not enough, however, and in 1807 a watercourse, which can still be traced, was dug from Raygill up the valley, across the beck and down to the mill. At the same time, Joseph Smith and partners were cutting ground for the foundations of a new calciner or roasting furnace, which they also built. Widow Smith, with her horse and cart, were leading clay to the mill. In 1810, a roller crusher at Forefield, on the Fryerfold Rake, was dismantled and rebuilt at the New Mill. This may have been for grinding either the ore or the slags or both.

The peat house stands on the crest of the scarp above and slightly west of the mill. It was an open sided structure, 390 feet long by 21 feet wide, and had a steeply pitched timber-truss roof, thatched with ling. It consists of 36 pairs of pillars, between six and nine feet high, with two gable end walls. Two internal partition walls split the structure into three sections of unequal length. These probably represent extensions. Cutting and carrying the peat was a major event and in 1817 some 75 people were involved in carrying 7159 loads of peat to the Surrender Mill. They were paid one shilling per load.

Building No.1 was single-storied and is split in two by a cross wall. Its southern room is thought to have been a store. The northern room has a fireplace and a recessed cupboard and is thought to have been an office.

Old Gang smelt mill – viewed from the south-west, c1935

The Old Gang Mill (No.2) is 73 feet long by 28 feet wide. Inside, at its west end, was a 24 foot diameter waterwheel, which drove blowing cylinders for the four ore-hearths on the north wall. The air main, from the cylinders to the hearths, probably ran in a duct behind the rear wall. The two small buildings (Nos.3 & 4) on the mill's south wall were lobbies for storing ore. The arches, which supported the fume hoods, are missing having been sold for £25 to the Stewards of Muker Chapel in 1933. The flues, one from each hearth, converged on the New Mill, but remained separate, with the two outer flues being taken on top of the middle pair to form a 'double-decker' structure of two pairs of flues, one pair directly above the other. The lower pair went through the southern hearth and rose up in the northern hearth. The upper pair climbed over the New Mill.

The hearths, which were recorded in the smelting accounts as A, B, C & D, were working two shifts per day in 1857, but soon afterwards this was reduced to one shift. The following example shows how much lead the four hearths made in a six day week.

Monday 4th to Saturday May 9th, 1857.

	Ore	Pcs	LEAD		
Hearth	Cwts	Lead	Cwt	Qr	Lbs
A	196	120	120	3	12
B	292	186	186	1	24
C	360	227	227	0	0
D	210	139	139	3	15
	1058	672	674	0	23
Slag B	47	21	21	2	22
Soot B	12	8	8	0	12
Waste D	134	70	73	0	1
	193	99	102	3	7

A picture of the population of upper

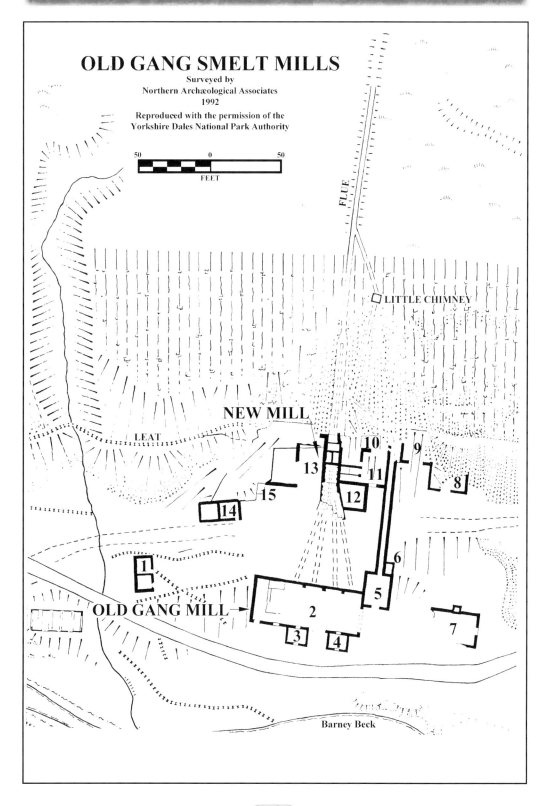

OLD GANG SMELT MILLS

Surveyed by
Northern Archæological Associates
1992

Reproduced with the permission of the
Yorkshire Dales National Park Authority

FEET

FLUE

LITTLE CHIMNEY

NEW MILL

LEAT

OLD GANG MILL

Barney Beck

Old Gang smelt mill – viewed from the south, c1950

Swaledale is being built up using a variety of sources. The following smelters are listed in the Old Gang accounts and can also be traced in the censuses for 1861 and 1871. They all lived within easy walking distance of the mill.

1859	Age in 1861	Address
William Pedley	51	Lodge Green
Thomas Pedley	19	Dunts
James Pratt	16	Feetham
John Pratt	62	Feetham
Michael Pratt	21	Smarber
John Sunter	40	Low Row
Joseph Sunter	42	Feetham

1867	Age in 1871	Address
Thomas Dolphin	18	Riddings
William Fawcett	29	Feetham
Thomas Sarginson	19	Reeth
Thomas Sunter	30	Low Row

The building (No.5) abutting the east end of the mill housed the slag hearth. It has a vaulted roof and the stonework at the rear of the hearth area is severely heat damaged. The slag-hearth's flue ran to the hillside, nearly 100 feet away, and then turned north-west to join the main flue.

Locally known as the 'Silver House', the building (No.7) with a tall chimney is not shown on the 1854 OS sheet. It was certainly never used for refining silver as the Old Gang

Old Gang smelt mill – viewed from the south, 1992 (YDNPA)

ore seldom had more than two or three ounces of it per ton, making it uneconomic to refine. The building may have housed an assay hearth, but it is much more likely to have held a small reverberatory furnace, used for softening the smelted lead. If so, it was built in the 1870s, when the Old Gang Company was getting complaints from lead merchants about the hardness of its lead. The process relied on melting pieces [ingots] of lead in the body of the furnace and keeping them molten for many hours. This gave the impurities chance to float to the surface and form a dross, which could be skimmed off. The lead was then recast into pieces. The extra cost of this process was, to some extent, offset by the added value of the purer product.

Building No.8 had two storeys and shows signs of plastering on its internal walls. There was an internal cupboard, similar to the one in building No.1, which suggests that it too was used either as an office or as a place for the smelters to lodge.

The complex of buildings and walls immediately east of the New Mill has been greatly altered, making them difficult to interpret. For example, part of the area under buildings 10 and 11 must have housed the waterwheel and bellows for the New Mill, of which no trace has yet been found. On the available evidence, however, the slag-hearth flue, which runs through the area, may have been joined by another one leading from building No.9. If so, this may be the site of a roasting furnace used in the Old Gang Mill's early years. In addition, the iron straps found in building 11 are so similar to the ones on the roasting furnace at the Surrender Mill as to suggest that it too held one. The chute which links buildings 10 to 11 suggests that the former was an ore lobby, used for storing ore prior to roasting it.

The interior of the Old Gang Mill and the area between it and the New Mill underwent considerable changes in the 1940s and 1950s, when a plant for recovering barytes from dump materials was built. This was a standard gravity mill, with a crusher, screens, jigs and vibrating tables. Unfortunately, the flues in this area were demolished and much detail lost.

The main chimney stood on Healaugh Crag, some 810 yards away, but there was also

Old Gang peathouse (YDNPA)

the Little Chimney on the scarp about 165 feet north of the New Mill. It stands about 12 feet high and is linked to the main flue by a short section of flue. The flue leading to it has, however, collapsed and become part of a larger scree which masks its lower course. The chimney is said to have been used at times when weather conditions caused a back-draught in the main flue.

In 1871 the company sought Thomas Bewick's advice on making good, soft lead. He blamed the ore-hearths, which got too hot and had to be left to cool for several hours each day. More fuel was then used to re-heat them, and more lead was lost through volatilisation. Also, because the tuyère's nozzle was too small for the volume of air supplied, the air blast was not distributed evenly throughout the fire. This made smelting inefficient by producing lead-rich slags which had to be smelted in the slag-hearth, at extra expense, and made poorer quality lead. The concentrates were between 75 and 76 per cent lead when fed into the ore-hearths, but only 60 per cent was recovered. The slags gave about two per cent and the fumes another three per cent, making a total yield of 65 per cent, or a loss of 10 per cent.

Bewick advised crushing the ore to a more uniform size, building a large roasting hearth to roast the concentrates before smelting, and building larger ore-hearths which, by dissipating the heat, could work continuously. In 1872, the agent and Mr Knowles, one of the partners, met Thomas Brown, a local stonemason, to discuss *"altering one of the [ore-] hearths similar as they have them in*

Arken[garth]*dale. We appointed Joseph White to assist him to pull the hearth down and assist him with the new"*.

As was usual, the mill was not suddenly closed, but it limped on for several years. We know that the mill smelted 267 tons of ore between May 1892 and October 1894, when the chimney was swept. In the latter month, however, Simon Cherry, the lessor's agent, remarked that *"owing to the poor produce made by smelting, it was thought advisable to sell the ore. Consequently no lead has been made during the last quarter"*. A further 181

Barras End Level, 1946

tons were smelted between April 1895 and October 1899, but from July 1898 onwards most of the ore was sold direct to smelters, especially John Walton & Company, at Castleside near Consett in County Durham. The very last ore to be smelted at the Old Gang Mill was for the February 1901 pay.

The AD Lessors kept the Old Gang smelt mill in repair, but when the roof of the roasting furnace house collapsed during gales in December 1910, the undamaged slates and timbers were stored in the mill, rather than repairing it. When it became clear that the industry was dead, Edward Cherry, their agent, was ordered to sell their roofs. This was done by auction on July 15th 1920.

Surrender Lead Mine

The boundary between the manors of Arkengarthdale and Healaugh which runs from Foregill Gate to Little Punchard Standard was in dispute in 1675. Of particular importance was an area called Wetshaw, which was being approached by rich mines from either side and was, therefore, likely to carry ore. John Bathurst, Lord of the Manor of Arkengarthdale, and Phillip Swale, the agent for Philip, Lord Wharton's Manor of Healaugh, rode the bounds, but they failed to agree. So the matter went to court.

At the first trial, evidence purporting to be an Inquisitional Survey of the Honour of Richmond, made in 1618, was produced and the case was settled in favour of Bathurst. In April 1699, however, Thomas, Lord Wharton's miners began sinking four double shafts and a single one at Wetshaw. That summer, Charles Bathurst leased mines in the same area to Sir William Robinson, whose miners also began sinking a shaft. Lord Wharton's men filled it in, nearly killing some miners who were underground, and attacked others on the surface. In October, Wharton told his agents to discharge Robinson's men and to *let them know, that I will call them to account for infringing the privilege of my peerage, if they shall after this warning persist in the same*.

In November, Wharton complained to the House of Lords *of the violence* [that] *hath been offered to me*" and they sent an officer to Yorkshire to arrest one of Robinson's partners, called Longstaff, and twenty other men. Wharton instructed Mathew Smales, his lawyer, to do nothing to warn people of the impending arrests, in case the miscreants should flee.

Robinson and partners then brought an action of ejectment against Wharton in the Court of Chancery. This case lasted for three years and saw a number of counter claims, with evidence being dismissed and then reallowed. When the verdict went against him, an enraged Wharton sent his men to Wetshaw to rip out all the ore they could. Robinson described them as *"multitudes of people hired and set on for that purpose, to a great loss and prejudice for the plaintiffs"*. In December 1702, the Court ruled that all the land east of Bleaberry Gill was part of the manor of Arkengarthdale and that Wharton *"in order to deprive the plaintiffs of the aforesaid suite has increased the numbers of workmen in the said pits so that in a sort time the veins or lodes of lead will be worked out"*. Wharton was forbidden from working any mines at Wetshaw.

Wharton then tried to get the survey of 1618 ruled ineligible by appealing to the House of Lords. It ordered a trial to determine whether the disputed evidence was the *"perfect, unaltered, exact and intire Commission and Return first filed in the Court of Exchequer in 1618"*. Lord Wharton was to be the plaintiff and Sir William Robinson Baronet, Charles Bathurst the Elder and others were defendants. The verdict, in November 1703, was that the evidence was eligible. A map showing the disputed boundaries was made in 1710, but the issue did not progress to a trial and the matter appears to have been put on the shelf.

Because of this dispute, there was very little mining at Wetshaw until 1797, when George Earl of Pomfret and Peter Denys took a

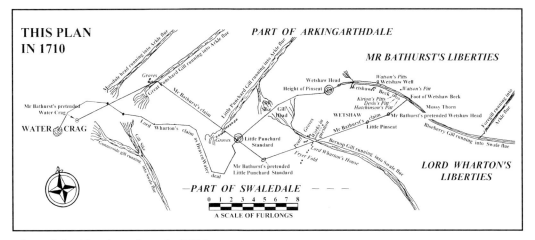

THIS PLAN
IN 1710

PART OF ARKINGARTHDALE

MR BATHURST'S LIBERTIES

Groves

Mossdale head running into Arkle flue

Great Punchard Gill running into Arkle flue

Little Punchard Gill running into Arkle flue

Wetshaw Head

Height of Pinseat

Mr Bathurst's claim

Watson's Pitts
Wetshaw Well
Watson's Pitt

Wetshaw Beck

Foot of Wetshaw Beck

Kirton's Pitts
Devis's Pitt
Hutchinson's Pitt

Mossy Thorn

WETSHAW

Mr Bathurst's claim
Mr Bathurst's pretended Wetshaw Head

Mr Bathurst's pretended
Water Crag

WATER CRAG

Lord Wharton's claim as Heaven Water

Gill Side

Gunnerside gill running into Swale flue

Gill Head

Groves

Peats

Groves

Brocks in agreement

Little Pinseat

Bernop Gill running into Swale flue

Blueberry Gill running into Swale flue

Foregill running into Arkle flue

Little Punchard
Standard

Mr Bathurst's pretended
Little Punchard Standard

Fryer Fold

Lord Wharton's House

deal

*LORD WHARTON'S
LIBERTIES*

—PART OF SWALEDALE — — —

0 1 2 3 4 5 6 7 8

A SCALE OF FURLONGS

Plan of the Wetshaw Area in 1710

quarter share in a new mine there with William Chaytor and John Breare. Soon afterwards, the AD Lessors and the Lords of Arkengarthdale agreed to settle the boundary dispute by arbitration. The arbitrators' decision that the boundary should follow its present course, much as Philip, Lord Wharton had claimed over a century before, was endorsed by the parties in March 1798.

The first ore from the new mine, which was called Surrender, no doubt in celebration of the agreement, was smelted in December 1797. Three years later Surrender had proved very rich and in November 1800 work began on *"repairing the old level out of Bleaberry Gill to drain the beds before starting the whim shaft".*

The High (later Old) Whim Shaft, which was within 40 feet of the boundary with the Old Gang, began in the Millstone Grit and ended about seven fathoms into the Main Limestone, at a depth of 67 fathoms. The New Whim Shaft, some 1075 feet to the east of the Old Shaft and 50 feet lower, was sunk before 1816. Because the beds dipped 12 fathoms between the Old and New Shafts, it was 60 fathoms deep to the middle of the Main Chert. Steep dips and a series of mineralised step-faults threw the bearing beds down to the south and west. This meant that the veins were reached from a series of crosscuts and sumps, and by 1816 the deepest

working was 122 fathoms below the shaft top. The mine was also very wet, which made it expensive to work, but most of the water was drained by natural cavities.

In 1801, Peter Denys proposed driving a level to work the Barras End veins, at the south-east end of the Old Gang sett. At first he planned to start between the New and Old Mills on Barney Beck, but, instead, he chose a site near Bleaberry Gill, at Foregill Gate, which would drain Surrender as well. In February 1802, however, Barras End Mine was idle, but the level must have begun not long afterwards and in June 1807 the water race from Bleaberry Gill to the Old Smelt Mills was repaired where it runs under Barras End hillock. When Messrs Alderson took over the Old Gang Mine in 1811, Barras End Level was 3100 feet long and was driven at a rising gradient of around 1 in 350. It would have reached the foot of the Surrender Old Whim Shaft at a depth of 105 fathoms, having risen two fathoms, but, as John Davies noted, this would only just drain the heavily flooded beds there. There was a bonus in early 1813, however, when Davies reported that the Arkengarthdale miners, working in Moulds Level, had followed Waterblast Vein almost to the Surrender boundary, where it carried a solid rib of ore 18 inches wide. Barras End Level would cut this vein around 1100 feet after crossing into Surrender ground.

Frederick Hall, who took over from Davies in May 1814, took the view that Barras End Level was only ever going to be of marginal benefit to Surrender, and had no place in his plans for the Old Gang Mine. He stopped driving it in July of that year and little, if any, work was done between then and July 1826 when James Spensley, the Surrender agent, and others surveyed the Old Gang workings.

The level was resumed when Messrs Jaques took on the Old Gang in August 1828, and they drove the remaining 360 feet to the boundary within a year. The Surrender Company drove it for some distance into their ground along Barras End Vein. Reform Level, sometimes called Barras End High Level, was also driven onto this vein from higher up the gill.

The key to working Surrender was still by extending Moulds Level across the boundary. It was around 100 feet lower than Barras End Level and it was already driven up to the boundary in Waterblast Vein. At this point, the level was in the 27 Fathom Grit on the north, or downthrow, side, and in the Main Limestone on the south side, so the level would have command of the bearing beds, which rise all the way to the Surrender Shafts. In 1841, therefore, the company, which had members in common with the Arkengarthdale Company, signed an agreement to do this. They paid £2100 for a 21 year wayleave, which gave them the right to use Moulds Level and to build a dressing floor near its mouth.

The mine's fortunes had fluctuated wildly, as the following comments, both by John Davies, show. In June 1813 he wrote that output at Surrender was good, and the mine was *"employing all the miners who go to them"*. In November 1813, however, it was poor. Nevertheless, the average annual output of lead between 1820 and 1831 was 335 tons. It then fell to 160 tons until 1843, when the Surrender Level from Moulds began to open new ground on Jacob North and Sun Veins, and on the Great Sun Vein. The latter was particularly rich and contributed to the output recovering to an average of 370 tons a year until 1850, and 455 tons until 1859.

It then fell off, and in 1863 Sir George Denys believed that the Surrender ground was almost worked out. Nevertheless, the company continued paying £20 per year wayleave for using Moulds Level and struggled on until 1868, when its lease expired.

As he did elsewhere, Sir George Denys kept a few men at work picking through the old workings. He was forced to lay them off in 1873, however, when Gilpin Brown, the Arkengarthdale mineral lord, withdrew the wayleave under the pretext that there was too much water coming out of Moulds Level in wet weather. The drainage was not stopped, as this would have been illegal, but it left no way of getting ore out of the mine.

This wayleave was never renewed, but later in 1873 the AD Lead Mining Company Ltd began work at Surrender, with miners getting ore in the old workings near the shafts. They agreed a wayleave with the Old Gang Company, which allowed the new company to use Hard Level to drive across the boundary from the Forefield area. In order to *"do away with the use of the Forefield Top Level"*, a connection was made to Pedley's Crosscut by a short inclined plane, which allowed horse-drawn waggons to be brought from Surrender into Hard Level. The company had also begun driving an incline down from the forehead of Barras End Level. This would eventually have got to the same horizon as the workings from Moulds and, when connected to them, would have provided a haulage route from the mine. It was stopped in May 1875, whilst a rise was made to get fresh air, but the work was never completed, possibly because the link with Hard Level was sufficient.

Output from Surrender averaged 60 tons of ore per year between 1873 and 1880, but the AD Company proposed closing the mine in August 1877, because it was short of funds and wanted to concentrate on raising ore from Fryerfold Vein, which had recently been cut in Sir Francis Level. It appears that Sir George stepped in again, because a few men were getting ore there until early 1882. In 1880, he was even planning to sink a sump

from the Surrender Level, with a water-pressure engine for pumping and winding. Possibly because Sir George died in February 1881, this scheme came to nothing.

In 1887, the AD Lessors gave permission for the Old Gang Company to drive Hard Level east in Forefield Sun Vein, across the Surrender boundary. This level was eight fathoms deeper than Forefield Level (in Fryerfold Vein) and the ground below it was dry, where it had previously been wet. As there were several veins to the north of this point that had not yet been worked in the Main Limestone, Simon Cherry proposed that the Surrender ground should be included in any new lease of the Old Gang. A little ore was also raised then, but Surrender remained closed.

Surrender Smelt Mill – Low Chimney, 1946 (YDNPA)

Arkengarthdale Mines

In 1068, King William dispossessed the Anglo-Saxon Lords and gave their lands around Richmond, which included Arkengarthdale, to Count Alan of Britanny.

The Lordship of Richmond was conferred on Richard, Duke of Gloucester (later Richard III), in 1473. The estate remained Crown property from his death in 1485 until 1628, when Charles I transferred the Lordships of Richmond to the citizens of London in return for settlement of loans made to himself and his father, James I (VI). Dr John Bathurst, who had acquired Clints by marriage in 1635, worked the Arkengarthdale Mines, first under the Commonwealth (1649 to 1653) and then under a lease from the Citizens of London from 1654. He bought Arkengarthdale in 1656, but still had to lease the minerals until they too were sold to him. At this time, ore from the Arkengarthdale Mines was smelted at Clints.

On the death of John Bathurst in 1659, the mines passed to his elder son, Charles, who was in poor health. The mines were, therefore, run by his brother, John, who held them on a lease from 1673. After Charles died without issue in 1680, the ownership of the mines was claimed by John, but this was disputed by his younger brother, Theodore. The latter claimed that his eldest son, also called Charles, who was the nephew and godson of the first Charles, was the rightful heir. This claim succeeded and Theodore oversaw the mines until his son came of age around 1699.

When the second Charles died in 1724, the mines passed to his son, another Charles, who died childless in 1740. His estate and the mines were then run by his widow, Ann, and William Turner, his sister Jane's husband. Ann Bathurst died in 1747 and, when all debts had been settled, the estate was split amongst the husbands of Charles Bathurst's three sisters. These men were William Sleigh of Stockton, William Turner of Kirkleatham, and Charles Francis Foster of Buston in Northumberland. The arrangements for working the mines were given in an agreement made between the joint Lords in January 1778, by which they each paid one-third of the mines' running costs and, in return, got one-third of the pig lead, which they were free to sell.

The first link with the Bathurst family was broken in 1808 when George Brown, a London banker who also had a share in the Blakethwaite Mine, bought William Sleigh's one-third share in the mines. Three years later George Brown bought the late Charles Turner's one-third share. When Brown died without issue in 1814, his two-thirds share of the Arkengarthdale estate passed to his sisters, Lady Elizabeth Preston and Jemima, wife of the Reverend John Gilpin. Lady Preston consolidated their ownership in 1821, when she bought Francis Foster's share. John Gilpin shared the running of the estate with Robert Clarke and William Sampson, the trustees who were appointed under George Brown's will.

John Gilpin died in the 1840s, when his son and heir, George, was a minor and so the estates were run by trustees until he came of age in 1854. In return for adding the name Brown to his own, George Gilpin also inherited the whole of the Brown family's estates from his aunt Elizabeth. George Gilpin

Brown died in November 1889 and was succeeded by his son, George Thomas Gilpin Brown. When the Arkengarthdale Mining Company's lease was not renewed, he took over the mines and ran them himself from 1891 to 1903. When he died in November 1918, the Arkengarthdale estate had already been sold. The new owners were more interested in the estate's sporting value and mining had ended by 1913.

THE MINES AND SMELT MILLS

There were lead mines in Arkengarthdale before the Norman Conquest, but it is not until 1285 that mining is recorded. In that year, the profits of the mines were valued at £4 per year. Thereafter, there are regular, if infrequent, references to mining in the accounts of Richmond Castle.

It is likely that these early miners worked under a form of customary law, by which they were granted a few meers of ground and kept possession of them for as long as they worked them regularly. The protection of these laws appears to be the purpose of a law of 1181/2 whereby anyone who paid a royalty to the Crown was free to search for lead in the waste. In 1233 King Henry II commanded Richard Fitton *"not to impede or permit any impediment to our workers in our manors of Swaledale and Wensleydale by which they may less be able to freely and expeditiously work there, as they were accustomed to do in the time of King Henry our grandfather and King Richard our uncle and King John our father"*.

The system began to change in 1509, when William Conyers of Marske got wider rights to search for lead in the wastes of Arkengarthdale and New Forest. In return, he was to pay the King a royalty of 1/9th. Conyers, whose mines were in the Punchard area, had his lease renewed for 21 years in 1531. The next year, all the mines not already let to Conyers were leased to Sir James Metcalfe, of Nappa Hall near Askrigg. Their

lead was smelted at bales on Moulds Side and Windegg Scars. The money arising from the rent and royalties of these leases was put towards the cost of the garrison at Berwick Castle.

When the last male heir of William Conyers died, in 1558, his Marske estates passed, through the marriage of an heiress, to Arthur Phillip. That part of Marske called Clints then became important to the development of mining in Arkengarthdale because lead raised in the latter place was smelted there until c1750. This aspect is covered in more detail in the section on Marske.

Dr John Bathurst worked the Arkengarthdale Mines, first under the Commonwealth (1649 to 1653) and then under a lease from the Citizens of London from 1654. His miners worked shafts on Windegg and made trials on Moulds Side. There is no mention of the earlier mines at Punchard. Benjamin Purchas, the agent for both John Bathursts, was paid a salary of £20 with an allowance of £30 towards expenses. Timber for the mines was cut in woods around Clints and stored in a locked building in Arkengarthdale. This was *"to keep the wood from the miners' fireside"*.

Thirteen men and one widow worked the mines and dressed their own ore, for which they were paid 19 shillings per horse load (2 cwts). The dressed ore was carried by jaggers to a store house at Gun Nest on the watershed between Slei Gill and Clints Beck. From there it was taken to Clints, and sometimes Gilling, for smelting. In the 14 months from August 1st 1657, the mines produced 469 horse loads (47 tons) of ore at a cost of £421 7s 6d. The pig lead made from that ore sold for between £13 10s 0d and £14 5s 0d per fother and raised £1056 15s 11d.

The group of mines on Moulds Side had become the largest producer by 1675 and new veins were still being found. The workings were also approaching the boundary between Arkengarthdale and Lord Wharton's manor of Healaugh, which ran up Bleaberry Gill from the ford at Foregill Gate. This had not been fixed precisely, however, and the potential value of the ground there lent

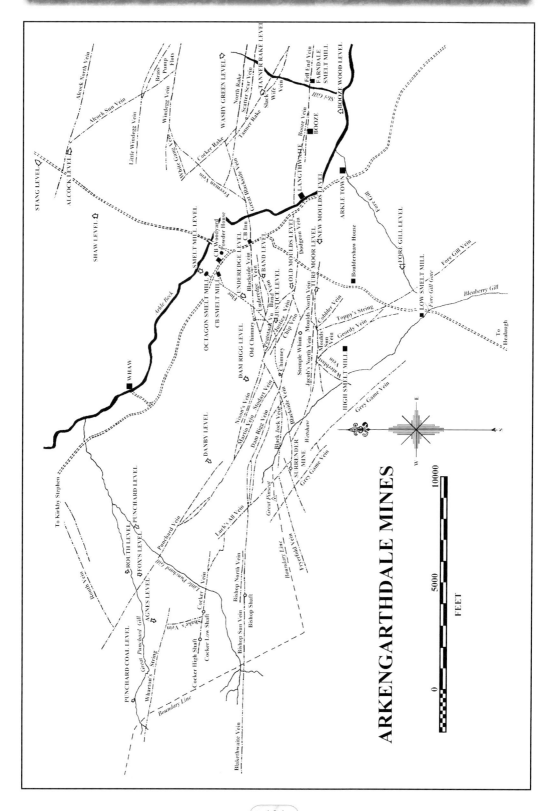

ARKENGARTHDALE MINES

0   5000   10000

FEET

urgency to the matter. Nevertheless, the parties could not agree and so the matter went to court, which found in Bathurst's favour. In 1699, therefore, he became a partner in a company set up to finance an expansion of the mines along the boundary at Moulds Side. Lord Wharton responded by sending miners to sink shafts alongside those of the new company. They also began back-filling one of the latter whilst miners were still underground, nearly killing them. Wharton's agent was also instructed to stop the Arkengarthdale miners working by giving them a warning called a discharge.

Lord Wharton raised the matter in the House of Lords, which sent an officer to arrest one of the partners and 20 of their men. The parties returned to court, but claim and counter claim meant that a judgement, this time for Wharton, was not given until December 1703. The argument, which appears to have petered out then, was not resolved until 1796.

The third Charles Bathurst's head agent was Thomas Smales of Gilling. In the first four years from 1724, when this Charles inherited, some 2,324 tons of grove ore, plus 731 tons of waste ore, were produced, showing that the mines were much richer than they had been in 1657.

Another interesting dispute, arising from what was probably a hangover from the days of working by customary law, began in 1731. The Rectory of St Mary's Church, Arkengarthdale had, of custom, a right to a tithe on all ore *"as it fell from the pick when it was dug in a mine in the parish of Arkengarthdale and such part as was small enough to pass through the mesh [of a one-inch riddle] was by custom exempt from tithe"*. After the Dissolution of the Monasteries, this and other rights were sold and were eventually acquired by the Lowther family in 1628.

Sir William Lowther claimed that Charles Bathurst's miners were deliberately breaking

Stoddart Hush

the ore smaller so that it would go through the riddle and so not be eligible to tithing. Evidence given in the case, which confirmed Lowther's rights, tells us that the tithable portion was often between one-seventh and one-eighth.

As output from the mines rose, the traditional method of computing the tithe ore became too time consuming. Easterby, Hall & Company sought to replace the tithe with a cash payment, but this did not happen until 1821. In that year, the Lowthers leased the right to collect the tithe to the mining company, in return for £200 per year for 21 years. This effectively stopped the tithing of lead ore.

In July 1738, what became Tanner Rake High Level had just been completed and soon afterwards a store was built nearby for the tithe ore. Also on the east side of the valley, several shafts were being worked at Windegg, as were the hushes known as Windegg, Tanner Rake, North and Scatter Scar. On the west side of Arkengarthdale, Moulds Side was still being developed, but North and Danby Hushes, plus shafts into the Undersets at Briggillburn, were all producing ore. A level was also being driven south from Little Punchard Gill. A rich strike at Punchard, probably on Bishop's Vein, where the vein was reported as being *"four feet wide of bouse"*, led to work being stopped elsewhere in order to free men to work it. The ore was said to be so clean that it could go directly from the mine to the smelt mill. A road, costing £300, was built to the mine at Punchard.

Sometime before 1719, with output from mines on the west side Arkengarthdale increasing, a new smelt mill, later called the Low Mill, was built alongside Bleaberry Beck a little upstream of the ford at Foregill Gate, in an area now popular with picnicking visitors. The mill had an ore-hearth and a slag hearth, housed in two buildings, and some of the pillars of the peat house can still be seen, built into the moor wall. When the Octagon Mill began smelting, around 1804, the Low Mill closed and part of it became a dwelling. Members of the Alderson family are recorded as living there from 1805 to 1830.

Early in 1780, the lord's senior agents Thomas Simpson and James Alderson were sacked for negligence and drunkenness respectively. Their replacement, a lawyer called Sampson George, was made Steward of the Manors of Arkengarthdale and New Forest.

The 1780s saw more of the Moulds Side veins being developed in the Underset Beds from deep whim shafts. The whim for Damrigg Whim Shaft, for example, cost £8 8s 0d and the sods used in building the horse circle cost a further £3 3s 0d in 1789. At this time shafts and levels were still being lined with timber where they went through loose strata. The use of dry-stone walling to support shafts and levels came into more general use in the early 19th century. Underground haulage had been improved by the introduction of waggons running on wooden rails, which also means that haulage ways were more extensive and were being driven to larger dimensions. Trap doors, which diverted air into pipes and forced it into dead ends, and water-blasts were used to improve ventilation. Where these methods could not be used, boys were employed to turn fans, which were also connected to air pipes.

In 1785, the joint lords built the High Smelt Mill, along with stores, an office, a smithy and a stamp mill, near Moulds Bottom. Water for the wheels driving the bellows and the stamps came from a nearby dam which, in turn, was fed by a ditch from the Wetshaw area. Like the Low Smelt Mill, it was replaced by the Octagon Mill.

Hushing was an important way of getting ore from near the surface, nearly always after the vein had been worked first from shallow shafts. As we have already seen, Windegg, Tanner Rake, North and Scatter Scar hushes, in the older part of the mines, were working in the 1730s. The dams associated with them had such exotic names as Bouncing Bill, Riverags, Roaring Meg and Tail Briches.

Few details of the cost and rewards of hushing have survived, but preparatory work for a new hush at Shaw, near the Stang road to Barnard Castle, cost the following in 1790:-

	£	s	d
Cutting 138 roods of tailrace			
at 6d per rood	3	9	0
Guttering 276 roods of tailrace			
at 2d per rood	2	8	6
Building a dam at the hush tailrace			
	9	9	0
Cutting a gutter from Hurgill Head			
to the dam 131 roods at 2d per rood			
	1	1	10

Joseph Stoddart's hush, the largest on Moulds Side, was begun in 1787 and produced lead worth £2500 in ten years. He then took a lease at Fremington, where it is thought he worked on the Fell End Hush.

Most of the ore was coming from the deep whim shafts, however, and these were reaching the limits of their effectiveness. By 1797, therefore, Sir Charles Turner's agent, a Stockton shipping agent called Mathew

Moulds Level (YDNPA)

Wadeson, was getting worried. In July, he wrote that *"lead is now beginning to be very much sought after, but the Arkendale mines alas are very poor"*. By January 1799, he wrote bleakly that the *"C.B. Mines are done, the prospects for the proprietors a gloomy one"*.

The lords responded by employing Robert Clarke and John Breare, both land agents, to consider ways of turning matters around. Their conclusions, which eerily mirrored those of a similar enquiry by the AD lords into the running of their mines, were that the underground agents were *"by no means equal to the conduct of the mines there under the present difficulties"*. Also, through *"a want of union and concert making trials at great expense"*, some £800 had been squandered on sinking a shaft that would never be *"of the slightest use"*. To this was added the recurring complaint, which dogged large parts of the industry, that way-gates had been driven too small and that proper records of them had not been kept. There was a catalogue of wastefulness and lax management, but to what degree there was a lack of direction from the lords themselves is, of course, not said. The answer for the owners of the C.B. Mines, as for those of the AD Mines, was to get out of the way and lease their mines to wealthy companies which were dedicated to the exploitation of the mineral using modern methods and approaches.

Thus it was that Easterby, Hall & Company began running the mines in January 1800. Frederick Hall, the mine manager and one of the partners, lived at Scar House. He was a dynamic man, but was described as having *"some reverse traits"*. Hall did not use the deep whim shafts, which were expensive to work, and by November 1800 was reported to be *"driving no fewer than nine horse levels and spending £300 per week"*. Of these, Moulds Level proved a number of rich veins in the Main and Underset Beds on the south side of the Blackside Vein. This fault, which has a considerable down-throw to the south, crosses Moulds Side and effectively divides the workings into two groups. Danby Level, on the north side of the fault, worked veins in the Main Limestone.

Octagon smelt mill, 1924

Eventually, two dressing floors were built at Moulds Level, one near its mouth and the other near Moor Intake Farm. Water for the equipment on the floors, which included roller crushers and hotching tubs, was brought in a leat from Punchard Gill.

At first, the ore was smelted at the High and Low Mills on Moulds Side, but they were both old and badly sited for access from Hall's new horse levels, which were driven from the valley side. In 1802, therefore, work began on a large, new mill around 650 feet north-west of the junction of the Stang road and the Reeth to Tanhill road. This mill, generally called the Octagon Mill because of its shape, began smelting in the spring of 1804. It was 107 feet long and 70 feet wide, making it one of the largest buildings in the Dales. Its six

ore-hearths, which could make around 75 tons of lead per week, were blown by machinery – probably a system of blowing cylinders because it is hard to see where there was room in the mill for bellows – bought from Boulton and Company of Soho, near Birmingham. The 36 foot diameter, overshot waterwheel, which drove the blowers, was built into the centre of the mill. Fumes from the hearths vented into massive flues which ran under the Reeth to Tanhill road and ended at a chimney on Moulds Side.

The Octagon Mill was maintained throughout the 19th century and, for a time, was used as a store by a local builder. When part of the mill collapsed in 1941, however, it was demolished.

Hall also built a six-sided powder magazine

Octagon smelt mill – roof timbers (L. Barker)

in the field between the Octagon Mill and the Stang road. Some of the houses and the wood yard in the same area may also date from this time because there was an influx of miners and their families. Nevertheless, Alderson's 1841 map of the dale shows that Messrs Jaques and company's wood yard and offices were at Rigg Yard, 1000 feet south of the C.B. public house.

Unfortunately, Easterby, Hall & Company were dogged by financial problems. In 1802, for example, they mortgaged their land in Arkengarthale in order to raise £3000 to cover development costs. In 1803, two of the partners, Aubone and John Surtees, were declared bankrupt following the failure of a bank in which they were also partners. In 1811 the remaining partners broke up, leaving rents, mortgages and tithes unpaid. Nevertheless, the Halls continued mining as part of a new company called the Arkindale and Derwent Mines Company, which had mainly London-based shareholders.

Most of the ore above Danby Level had been worked out by 1816 and so an 11 fathom deep underground shaft had been sunk to an under-level. Ore and rock were raised from the shaft by a horse whim in an underground chamber. Water normally drained into the Underset Limestone, but the workings flooded in wet weather. To remedy this, the company was driving two existing levels northwards, across the Blackside Vein, to give extra depth. Turf Moor Level, which was 20 fathoms lower, would work the Underset Beds, while Moulds Level, some 46 fathoms lower, would give access to the Third and Fourth Limestones.

The Arkindale and Derwent Mines Company never made a profit and was dissolved on September 1st 1817, with Walter Hall and Richard Puller Jnr, two of the partners, buying its plant and property for £9287 12s 5d. They kept the mines working, but at a much reduced scale, and so many miners faced hard times. This was especially so for those who had moved into the area to work for Easterby, Hall & Company and had no land. The company's lease expired in 1821, with little chance of a renewal, and so its last years were spent ripping out the available ore and doing little, if any, development of new reserves.

On June 6th 1821, the mines were leased

to a new company. Because he had a share in the Surrender Mine, however, John Gilpin reserved the right to extend any level or shaft across the boundary to both drain it and provide haulage routes. In particular, he contributed to the upkeep of Moulds Level and, in return, was allowed to take water from Foregill Beck for a dressing floor.

The partners in the new company were:-

Robert Jaques	Easby near Richmond
William Close	Richmond
Ottiwell Tomlin	Richmond
Mathew Whitelock	Cogden Hall, Grinton
Edmund Alderson Knowles	
	Low Row
John Birkbeck	Low Row

The duty was set at 1/6th on all lead produced, and they were to make pays twice yearly and employ no fewer than 130 experienced miners, of whom at least half were to live in the dale. They were also to drive Little Punchard Level southwards to the boundary with Healaugh and begin a level in the Main Limestone from the foot of Tanner Rake Hush. The latter level would both prove the North and Blackside Veins at depth and drain the old workings there. The Stang area was to be prospected by hushing.

There must have been some problem with using the Octagon Mill, because the lessors agreed to build a new smelt mill within nine months of the lease being signed. This was the New or C.B. Smelt Mill, and the site chosen for it was on the edge of the moor, across the road from the C.B. Yard. Allowing time for the mill to be built, it must have begun smelting in late 1822 or early 1823.

The C.B. Mill had two smelting rooms, each with three hearths. These backed onto a central, arched passageway which carried air pipes from a double-acting air pump, and

Octagon smelt mill, 1946

Powder house near Langthwaite

the flues. The air pump and the 33 foot diameter waterwheel were both housed in a room built on to the mill's north-east wall. Peat, which was burned in the ore-hearths, was kept in a building with large, arched openings which ran from the mill to the Tan Hill Road.

Besides its ore- and slag-hearths, the mill also had a roasting furnace, and all their fumes were led, via a 525 foot long double flue, into the disused Octagon Mill's flue.

This flue ran for 2340 feet to a chimney, but some time after 1854 it was extended to another chimney on Moulds Top.

When first built, the two smelting rooms were symmetrical on either side of the central, arched passageway, but in 1854 or early 1855 the southern room was extended by 15 feet to make space for the installation of a double-reverberatory furnace in the summer of 1855. Designed by an experienced smelter, Alfred Jenkins, who claimed that it would give considerable savings, the furnace had two linked compartments. The first compartment was a typical reverberatory furnace, with its own firegrate, while the second one took the waste heat from the first and used it to roast the ore, giving, it was claimed, a saving on coal. Modern experience suggests that the furnace would have been difficult to operate and unlikely to give anything like the economies claimed of it. This was because the smelting was done at between 900° and 950° Centigrade and had a moderately reducing atmosphere, whereas roasting was done at between 700° and 750° Centigrade, with an oxidising atmosphere. Control of the air flow, to maintain these conditions, would have taxed the smelters' skills.

CB Smelt mill, c1903

Ore-hearths at the CB smelt mill, 1946 (J.O. Myers)

A second patent, which included improvements in the furnace design, was granted in 1858. It is likely, however, that the trial of the Jenkins furnace only lasted for, at most, a few years, as output, which peaked in the mid-1850s, fell steadily thereafter. For its final 30 years or so, therefore, the C.B. Mill appears to have worked with just the three hearths in the north smelting room. Smelting stopped in spring 1903, when George Thomas Gilpin Brown abandoned the mines. In 1930, the smelt mill was described as being nearly derelict, with two stone built sheds used as garages. At the same time, the peat house was a cart shed and there was "*a large quantity of valuable dressed stone*". Today, the site is little more than a pile of rubble.

Jaques & Company were rich and began many new developments, engendering such an air of optimism that by the late 1820s it was said that "*not a house is empty*" in Arkengarthdale. The markets, however, were not so optimistic and, from a high of £25 6s

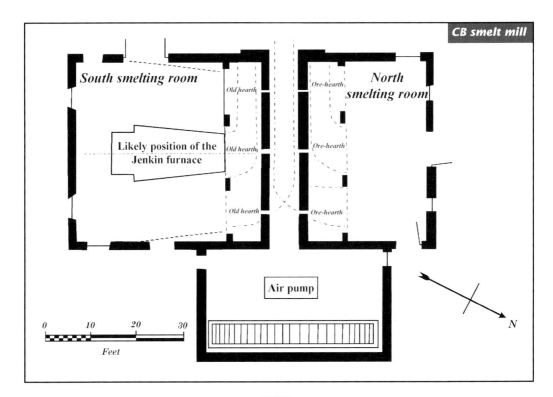

0d per ton in 1825, the price of lead fell steadily until it bottomed at £11 13s 0d per ton in 1832. There are few records of this period, but the company must have kept up its efforts because no fewer than 26 major levels were recorded in 1841 – 10 on the south

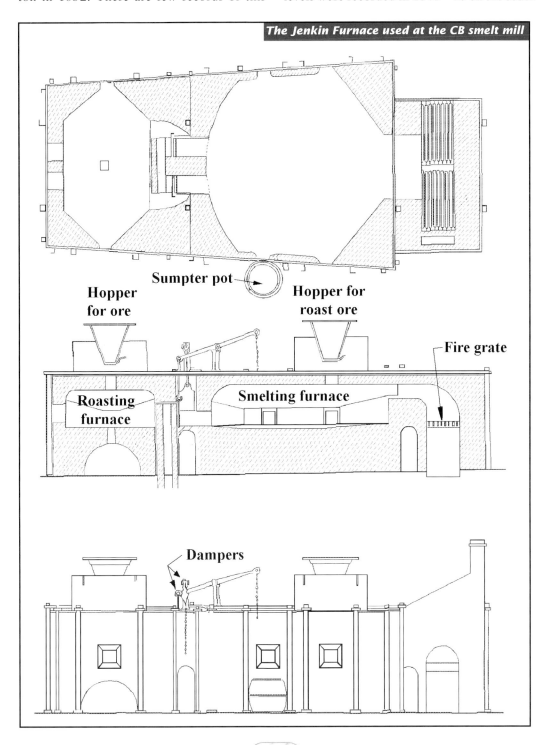

The Jenkin Furnace used at the CB smelt mill

Sumpter pot

Hopper for ore

Hopper for roast ore

Fire grate

Roasting furnace

Smelting furnace

Dampers

side of the dale and 16 on the north.

The option of a wayleave from Moulds Level to Surrender was taken up in 1841 because Robert Jaques and George Robinson were partners in both mines. The Surrender Company paid £21,000 for a 21 year wayleave, which gave them the right to use Moulds Level and to build a dressing floor near its mouth. A branch of Moulds Level, called the Surrender Level, was driven along Waterblast Vein to the boundary and on into Surrender Mine. This wayleave was withdrawn in 1873 on the pretext that too much water was coming out of Moulds in wet weather, but there was also some animosity between George Gilpin Brown and Sir George Denys.

The following snapshot of the mines in 1863 has been compiled from the report of a Government Commission, which visited the area, and an internal report on the condition of the mines.

Danby Level was the principal mine, with between 60 and 70 men working in it. Nevertheless, large parts of the workings were inaccessible, too small or without rails. The horse level forehead was about half a mile from the level mouth and was being driven by six men. There was no air shaft and the only ventilation came from fissures in the limestone, which tended to suck air into the mine. The ore workings were about nine fathoms above the level and were reached by climbing on stemples in a very wet rise.

Dam Rigg Level, which began in the Underset beds, had been driven about a mile since it was begun in Frederick Hall's time. Four men were working at the forehead, to which air was brought in zinc pipes from a ventilation rise about 180 feet away.

In Punchard Level, a large part of the workings on Cocker's String, Cocker Sun Vein and Shakes Vein could not be entered because of roof falls.

Routh Level, which was driven north from Great Punchard Gill, was also a mile long. Four men were making a rise, then 30 fathoms high, which was ventilated by fissures in the rock.

Moulds Level was almost abandoned, with two men picking over the ground, but it was kept open to ventilate Foregill and Turf Moor Levels, to which it was linked.

Fifty men were working at Foregill Level on a 600 foot long stretch of vein which ran southwards from its intersection with the level. These workings were ventilated by using a trap door to force air into an under-level, which was eight fathoms below the horse level and connected to it by sumps. There was also a rise to Turf Moor Level, which was idle, but kept open for ventilation. A crosscut, which was being driven west from near Foregill Level mouth, was ventilated by a windy king.

Aerial view of CB and Octagon smelt mills

CB Yard, c1920

On the east side of the dale, Tanner Rake Low and Middle Levels and Doctors Level, off Slei Gill, were all inaccessible because of roof falls. This and the Windegg area appear to have been abandoned.

By contrast, the development of the Faggergill area was just beginning. At Faggergill Level, two teams of two men were driving the forehead, which was nearly a mile and quarter from the mouth.

At the forehead of Stang Level, six men, four on one shift and two on the other, were driving a cross drift southwards from the top of a four fathom high rise. The drift was 240 feet long and had no means of ventilation. Another twelve men were working in another rise, about three fathoms above the horse level.

The company's neglect of repairs to the mines and buildings led to a claim being lodged for damages against its surviving partners in 1873. The outcome of the case is not known, but it is clear that the old order, which had monopolised mining in the two dales for around 40 years, was losing its grip.

Besides the growing poverty of its older mines, the company faced another problem at Whitsuntide in 1864, when the Sunday was a glorious day, but the Monday saw a massive thunderstorm with torrential rain. Bridges were washed away and houses flooded and *"at several of the lead mines, the waggons and everything movable were borne off by the flood, and the shafts inundated and filled with sand"*.

Soon after 1863, Booze Wood Level was started from near the side of the Arkle Beck. It was driven nearly due north and was intended to try the Booze (Fell End) Vein in the Fourth (Five Yard) Limestone.

In late September 1867, the *Darlington & Stockton Times* reported that the Arkengarthdale miners had struck, for the first time ever, following changes to the bargain system under which they were paid. The outcome of their action is not known, but the company was clearly trying to cut its costs. Thomas Raw, the agent for Jaques and Company, must have realised that the end was coming and had recently moved his family to Patterdale in the Lake District, where he worked at the Greenside Mine. What was left of the old company gave up the mines in 1869 and they were replaced by William Whitwell, of Jolson Hall in Westmorland. He became a partner in the Arkengarthdale Lead Mining Company, which was formed in July 1870:- Almost immediately, the company introduced new rules which obliged the men to work six hour shifts, six days a week, and also forced them to begin work at 7 a.m. or be fined for lateness. This was seen as an attack on the lead miners' independence and interfered with their small-holding or farming interests. When the company began enforcing fines on late comers in December 1870, the men struck, but were forced back to work after eight weeks. It is said that around 50 men left the dale rather than accept this imposition.

The previous company had been developing the Faggergill area and it was

footwall, but, although the vein was followed for 1200 feet, it proved a disappointment.

Work also continued at Booze Wood Level, which cut the Booze, or Fell End, Vein in April 1872. In the summer of the following year, a new dressing floor was built near the foot of Slei Gill. Waggons from the mine were taken, via a bridge over the track, to the top of some new bouse-teams. From these, ore was fed into a waterwheel-powered roller crusher, which had been bought from Appleton Charlton & Company of Ripon for £261 4s 0d. More plant for the floor was bought from the Bolton Parks Mining Company in Wensleydale for £266 10s 0d. Slime pits were also built to recover the finest particles of ore and prevent them from polluting the Arkle Beck.

Hon. Charles Wentworth Fitzwilliam	Aldwalton, Northants
William Frogatt Bethel	Rise, Yorkshire
George Thomas Gilpin Brown	Magdelen College
William Whitwell	Jolson Hall, Westmorland
Thomas Whitwell	Stockton
George Coates Whitwell	Stockton

The mine was badly ventilated because of its depth, and Charlton & Company supplied two windy kings for £11 15s 0d. One of these machines is now on display at the Museum of Yorkshire Dales Lead Mining, at Earby. At a later date, building stone and roofing flags were also quarried from the sides of Booze Wood Level.

In common with Sir George Denys at the Sir Francis Level, the Arkengarthdale Lead Mining Company replaced blackpowder with

hoped that some of the veins would cross the watershed into Scargill, where miners were also making a trial. The new company continued the work and, in 1874, were rewarded with a good find of ore at Faggergill. There was also a rich find in Danby Level. Slack's Crosscut was also driven northwards, from Stang Level, to try veins in the Hurgill area, which had also been tried from Faggergill Old Level.

Other trials being made were an extension to Harker's Level on Scar Top and the Smelt Mill Level. The latter was driven south-west, from the side of the Arkle, underneath the Octagon Smelt Mill. This was a deep trial of the Blackside Vein, below the Middle Limestone on the

Dynamite store near Langthwaite (YDNPA)

Waterwheel at Booze Wood Level dressing floor (L. Barker)

dynamite for blasting, but did not progress to compressed air drilling. The dynamite magazine can still be seen near the cattle-grid on the Tan Hill road.

When the Arkengarthdale Lead Mining Company's lease was not renewed, the mineral lord, George Thomas Gilpin Brown, took over the mines and ran them himself from 1891 until they fizzled out in 1903. The good days were over, however, and work seems to have concentrated on cleaning out the old workings. Output fell steadily, by around 40 tons a year, from 467 tons of lead in 1891 to 51 tons in 1902. The last lead was smelted in the spring of 1903 and the mines closed soon afterwards.

There was still interest in the mines, however, and in March 1907 a take-note, with the option of a 21 year lease, was issued

to a partnership headed by James Backhouse. They registered two new companies on October 26th 1907, with Thomas Harker of Yew Tree House as the manager of both. The 'CB' Lead Mines Ltd, with a capital of £7500 divided into £1 shares, was to prospect the common land to the west of Arkle Beck. Some work was done at Little Punchard, Routh and Agnes Levels, but the venture stopped in July 1909 and the company was wound up in 1915.

The second company, which was larger than the first, worked the Faggergill-Stang complex and had more success. It was the Stang & Cleasby Lead Mines Limited, with a capital of £20,000 divided into £1 shares.

The first six months was spent repairing the mines and getting them ready for working. The dressing floor at Stang Mine was also rebuilt and wooden huts erected over the machinery, which included a crusher, hotching tubs and buddles.

The main workings were at Faggergill, where the No.3 Level was reopened and driven towards a vein found in the Nut Hole/Sloate Hole Mine. A railway was built from the level mouth to the dressing floor at No.1 Level, which had been refurbished. Work at No.3 Level stopped at the end of 1909, however, when the men were transferred to the Nut Hole/Sloate Hole Mine. An earlier company had begun a level from the bottom of a shakehole, called Nut Hole, but had given up before proving the ore-body. Driving was resumed and, in October 1908, a second level was begun from a neighbouring shakehole, called Sloate Hole. In 1909 the two levels were linked to the dressing floor at Faggergill No.1 Level by a 600 yard long railway.

In 1909, the mines produced 150 tons of ore, most of it from Sloate Hole, and the future looked promising. The company was short of capital, however, and development work was delayed. As a result, output fell, with 77 tons of ore in 1911 and 18 tons in 1912. Efforts to raise more cash, including a possible new company, came to nought and the company gave up in 1914. This was the end of, at least, 800 years of lead mining in Arkengarthdale.

Fremington Mines

The manor of Fremington passed to the Parr family of Kendal in 1512, but was confiscated by the Crown in 1553 after the family supported the cause of Lady Jane Grey. The manor was returned the next year, when Parr was pardoned by Queen Mary, but on his death it became Crown property.

The answer to the question of who was the rightful lessor of the Fremington mines is confused, as, although they were generally included in the Crown's grants of the Grinton mines, a branch of the Wharton family from Gilling worked them from 1597 until 1746, and their heirs mortgaged them in 1796. The Whartons' rights (whatever they were) appear to have been bought by Thomas Swann, a banker from York who was one of the mortgagees, in 1827, because in that year he claimed the right to collect duty lead.

Unfortunately, no record of output or of duty lead payments has survived from this period, but the Crown dropped its claim to the minerals in 1834, when the Crown Commissioners accepted they had no legal title to them. The ownership of the minerals apparently passed, though on what pretence is not clear, to the Swanns who granted a number of leases in the 19th century.

THE MINES

The north-east side of Lower Arkengarthdale is dominated by the impressive line of Fremington Edge, a scarp slope topped by the Main Limestone. Copperthwaite, Jingle Pot and Hind Rakes, all of which were also worked at the Hurst Mines, outcrop on this slope. At its north-western end, where it is cut by Slei Gill, some of the principal veins off Moulds Side cross the beck and run up Fell End and on into Hurst. Here, the Fell End Hush is particularly noticeable.

In February 1583 the Fremington and Grinton mines were leased to Henry, Lord Scrope, and Arthur Phillips. Their ore was smelted at Phillips' smelt mill alongside Marske Beck at Clints. Soon after Arthur Phillips died in 1597, the Crown re-let the mines to Humphrey Wharton, who bought the Gillingwood estate near Richmond in 1609 and built his own smelt mill there.

When his lease of the mines was renewed for 21 years in 1629, Wharton took Henry, Lord Scrope as his partner. They worked the mines at Fell End and Reed Gutters, as well as on Copperthwaite, Jingle Pot and Hind Rake Veins.

The only known smelt mill in Fremington was probably built around 1625 by Humphrey Wharton. This was the New, or Farndale, Smelt Mill, which stood in Slei Gill, on the opposite side of the stream from the foot of Tanner Rake Hush. The mill, which appears in the 1625 accounts of Storthwaite Hall as follows *"item, for work tools and for bellows about the smelting house 30 shillings"*, is shown as a single building, with a waterwheel at its southern end, on a map made in 1718.

By 1729 Farndale Mill was run by a company of six men, who split it into 12 shares. Five of the partners held 11 shares between them, while the other partner, the third Charles Bathurst, had one. In August of that year, however, Bathurst bought out his partners and became the sole owner. An interesting aspect of this sale is the inclusion of a peat house at a time when the other mills in the area were still burning chopwood.

Curiously William Wharton, as lessee of the mines, was not a party to this sale, suggesting that his Gilling Mill was still in use. It is also unclear what use (if any) Charles Bathurst made of the mill, although it was well placed to serve his mines around the Tanner and North Rakes Hushes.

The Wharton family worked the mines until 1746 and their heirs mortgaged them in 1796. Also in that year, a lease was granted to Joseph Stoddart who, in October of the following year, was ordered to quit working the hush named after him on Moulds Side. As this man specialised in hushing, it is likely that he worked the Fell End Hush.

Spence & Company were granted a 14 year lease in 1814. They drove Fell End Level and are said to have raised 25,000 pieces, which was between 1250 and 1650 tons of lead.

The near monopolisation of the mining field by Robert Jaques and Company was completed in 1829, when they added Fremington to their leases of Old Gang, Surrender, Arkengarthdale and Hurst. Working as the Arkengarthdale Company, they continued Fell End Level beyond the boundary with Hurst and linked up with workings on Wellington and Blucher Veins. To deal with the ore it produced, a waterwheel-powered crushing mill was built at the level mouth. Around 1860, a crosscut north from the level found no workable ore in Black Vein.

Jaques and Company, who also worked Smithy, Haggs, Gutters, Scraes, Copperthwaite and Jingle Pot Levels, did not give up the Fremington mines in 1842, when they gave up the Hurst Mines, but instead kept them until 1868.

Around 1855, they completed Sun Gutter Level, which had been driven in search of Scatter Scar Vein, but had stopped without finding it. The vein was found after a short drive, but rises into the Main Limestone showed it to be barren and work stopped in March 1863.

In December 1865, a new level was begun in the grit above the Fourth (Five Yard) Limestone to prove the Copperthwaite Vein at depth. When Copperthwaite Sun Vein was reached, however, the Fourth Limestone was above the level, because of a number of ground slips, and it had to be proved from Bell's Rise. The level was abandoned in March 1871.

Next on the scene was the Fell End Company, which was granted a 21 year lease by the Swann family in May 1871. The partners in this company, who also had shares in the Grinton Mines, were:-

George Roper	Richmond
James Robinson Tomlin	Richmond
Hutton Simpson	Richmond
Richard Bowes	Richmond
James Knowles	Low Row
E.A. Knowles	Low Row
John Leonard Tomlin	South Kensington
Joseph Brown	Oldham

They were to start a new level from the side of the beck near Storthwaite (Sturfitt) Hall and drive north to cut Fell End Vein. The level began in or near the Third Limestone, but it was below the Fourth Limestone on the footwall when it reached the vein in April 1874. The vein proved poor at this horizon, as was Scraes Vein to the north of it, which was tried by a rise from a crosscut. Storthwaite Hall Level was abandoned in August 1878, but the company apparently limped on until 1883, when it closed its mines after producing 33 tons of ore.

Grinton Mines

THE MINERAL LORDS

Lead mining may already have been important when the massive cross-valley dyke system, known as the Grinton-Fremington dykes, was built to mark the boundary between British and Anglian peoples between the fifth and seventh centuries. There is no record of it until Norman times, however, when the Honour of Richmond, which included Swaledale, was held by Count Stephen of Brittany. When his daughter, Maude, married Walter de Gant Grinton was given as part of her dowry in return for military service at Richmond Castle. In 1125 Maude gave Grinton Church and some land for its upkeep to Bridlington Priory. Subsequent grants gave the priory land which extended to Havardale Beck and became the manor of Grinton. The mineral rights, however, were excepted and eventually passed to the Crown.

After its dissolution in 1537, some Bridlington Priory land reverted to the Crown, but the enclosed areas had been held on Customary Tenure, by leases, since 1483. The rectory and tithes of the Church of St Andrew at Grinton were farmed out in return for £41 annually.

With the exception of the Commonwealth period (1649 – 1653), when they were confiscated by Parliament following the execution of King Charles, the minerals were then held by the Crown until 1876, when Joseph Charlesworth paid £4000 for them.

THE MINES AND SMELT MILLS

The Grinton mines, on the south side of Swaledale, have been worked in six areas. From east to west, these are: Grinton Moor, Grinton How, Grovebeck, Harkerside, Whitaside and Summer Lodge. Unlike the north side of Swaledale, where the ore was found in regular veins, the ore at Grinton was mostly found in flots which, whilst rich, seldom lasted long.

The first specific reference to mining at Grinton was in 1504 when Christopher Conyers left *"halfe a more mere at Whitnowsyke* [Whitaside] *in the workyng of James Atkinson and half another more mere in the working of Edmund Tod"* to his wife, Elizabeth.

The Metcalfe family, of Nappa in Wensleydale, were the principal lessees of the Crown mines in the Honours of Richmond and Middleham and in 1531 Sir James Metcalfe took a new lease of them for 21 years, paying 1/9th duty. The income thus generated was used to pay the garrison at Berwick Castle.

The mediæval miners smelted their ore at wind-blown hearths, called bales, which were built on hillsides to catch the prevailing wind. Bale sites have been found on Harkerside and at Smeltings, on Grinton How.

In 1583 Henry, Lord Scrope and Arthur Phillips took a 21 year lease of the Harkerside and Whitaside mines at an annual rent of 20 shillings and a fine of £40. The Fremington mines, on the north side of the Swale, were also included in their lease. The lead from

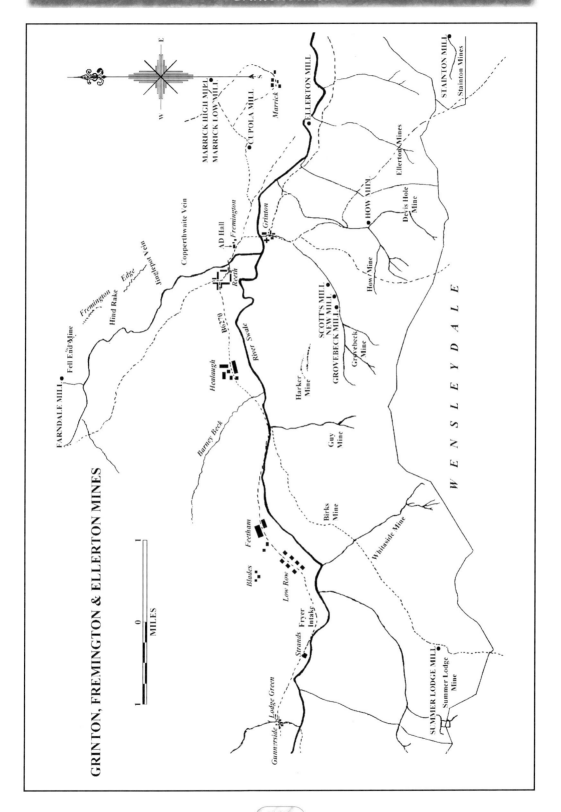

GRINTON, FREMINGTON & ELLERTON MINES

both groups of mines was smelted at Phillips' smelt mill in Clints. Phillips' father, James, who was an officer for the Royal Woods, Mines and Lands, was described as a dominating and thoroughly unscrupulous man who forced people into expensive lawsuits, often bankrupting them and enabling him to get their property cheaply. At Grinton, he was accused of plundering the woods and selling the timber for his own gain.

The mines reverted to the Crown in 1597 when Arthur Phillips died, but they were soon granted to Humphrey Wharton, who was Receiver General of Land Revenues for the Archdeaconary of Richmond and the counties of Durham and Northumberland. His lease was renewed in 1628, when his partner was Henry, Lord Scrope.

Humphrey Wharton belonged to a branch of the Wharton family which owned the mines in the manor of Healaugh, across the valley. He bought the Gillingwood estate, near Richmond, in 1609 and built the Gilling Smelt Mill, where ore from Grinton was smelted.

In 1649, when Parliament confiscated all Crown property, the Grinton mines, which were being worked without a lease by two local families, were valued as follows:

	£
Grinton	6
Harkerside	20
Whitaside	22
Fremington	12

The Swales, who had been at Grinton since 1157 and lived at Swale Hall, worked Harkerside and Whitaside. The Hillarys, of Grinton, worked on Grinton Moor. In 1692, Sir Solomon Swale leased the Harkerside Mine to Phillip Bickerstaffe, of Northumberland, and Charles Middleton and Thomas Ellerker, both of London, for 31 years at a duty of 1/10th. Sir Solomon and the three partners were each to invest £20 in the works. Ellerker died the following year, however, and it is thought likely that the partnership was dissolved after a dispute about rights to his share.

The foregoing events also sparked a series of law suits about mining rights. In 1696, Sir Solomon Swale served an order of ejectment against Roger Hillary, whose response was that his grandfather had bought the wastes and other lands in 1622 and this gave him title to the minerals. Moreover, his family had worked the coal pits, without interruption, since 1622 and had worked the lead mines on Grinton How for the previous six years, raising a large amount of lead in the process. Sir Solomon Swale counter-claimed that his manor of West Grinton included the mines.

The court ruled that Hillary's claim was invalid because the mines were reserved to the Crown in the sale of 1599, but his right to the wastes and coal mines was upheld. Swale was ordered to give an account of the profits from the mines during his occupation of them.

The absence of a lease brought in another party, Reginald Marriott, Auditor of the Crown Land Revenue. In 1660 his nominee, George Tushingham, had leased the mines, but failed to prevent Hillary and Swale's usurpation of them. In 1696, on the basis of their Crown lease, their sub-lessee, John Ozell, brought an action of trespass and ejectment against Sir Solomon Swale in the Exchequer of Pleas. When York Assizes heard the case, it found in Ozell's favour. Swale appealed, but lost again - so confirming the Crown's rights to the minerals.

This was not the end of disputes, however, and in September 1705 Thomas, the fifth Lord Wharton, who was in cahoots with Solomon Swale, ordered his miners to sink a shaft next to one of Marriott's on Grinton How. Marriott sought the protection of the courts. He got this and Wharton, Marriott and others were placed under a penalty of £1000 should they defy the order.

Some of Wharton's miners were also served with injunctions, but they ignored them. They dammed water leats, took over a smithy on Grinton How and began sinking three shafts on the major veins. Unfortunately, one of the shafts broke into a large spring of water and flooded all the other shafts around it.

Mathew Sissons, of Ripon, served more

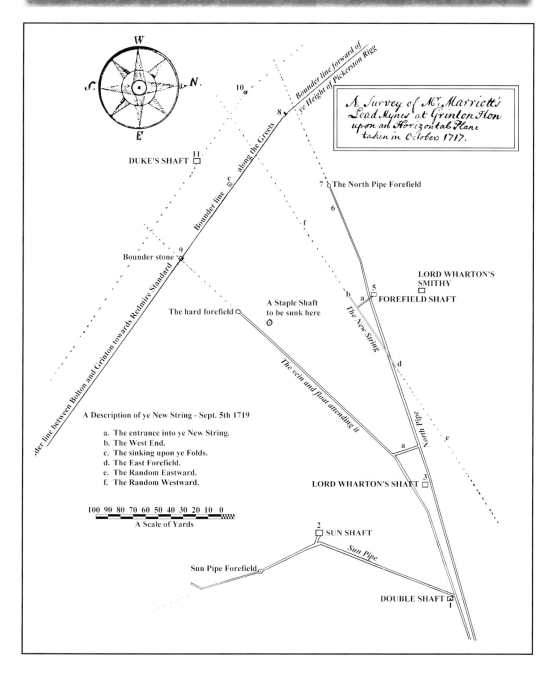

A Survey of Mr. Marriott's Lead Mynes at Grinton Hon upon an Horizontal Plane taken in October 1717.

A Description of ye New String - Sept. 5th 1719

    a. The entrance into ye New String.
    b. The West End.
    c. The sinking upon ye Folds.
    d. The East Forefield.
    e. The Random Eastward.
    f. The Random Westward.

100 90 80 70 60 50 40 30 20 10 0
A Scale of Yards

injunctions in May 1706, but the men's response was that *"they care not a fig for the injunctions"*. One of them, a John Sheldon, shot at Sissons' party with a fowling piece and chased them as far as Harkerside.

Wharton claimed Grinton as part of the land either granted to his ancestors or bought by them from Sir Thomas Vachell and John Molineaux. When the case reached court in London, both sides bribed members of the jury to sway the decision, which went in Marriott's favour.

Sir Solomon Swale's case, which was also rejected, was that Grinton was not really a

Grinton How Smelt Mill (L. Barker)

like earlier lessees who had smelted at Clints and Gilling, he was forced to use other mills. He may have used the nearby Ellerton mill or Bobscar mill in Apedale, and it is recorded that he used the Duke of Bolton's Mill and the Cupola Mill, both at Marrick. Between 1705 and 1710 Marriott bought large areas of land and the manorial title to the unenclosed wastes in Grinton. He probably built his own smelt mill soon after the last purchase, but it is not mentioned until 1722.

The mines continued to decline in the 1720s and, after Reginald Marriott's death in 1730, his son, Hugh, sought to sell the manor and the unexpired part of the Crown's lease. During 1733 he was in negotiations with the London Lead Company and they agreed a purchase price of £2635, but the deal fell through, probably because the company discovered that Marriott had no right to sell the Crown lease.

manor, but had only been called one by ministers of the Crown after the dissolution of Bridlington Priory. He died, ruined and brokenhearted, in December 1733 after spending time in prison for debt, much of which arose from his law suits.

Marriott was then free to develop the mines, especially those on the How. He employed Roger Bayne as barmaster at a salary of £10 per year to oversee the granting of ground to miners. The mines proved expensive to run, however, and Marriott was left with a profit of only £462 9s 0d on an income of £2948 3s 10d in the first 18 months or so from July 1697. Despite heavy expenditure, output from the mines fell from 1709 onwards.

Marriott had no smelt mill at Grinton and,

In 1736, however, the lease, but not the smelt mill, was acquired by Edmund Moore, a mine adventurer from Redruth. He installed Thomas Rosewarne as his agent at Grinton, and spent heavily on the mines there. In particular, he began sinking sumps and shafts in order to develop the veins in the Underset beds. As a result, when he asked for a new lease, he was granted one for 23½ years from the end of the old one in 1750.

Edmund Moore's share in the mines was split into three when he died in 1752. One third went to his wife, Frances, another third to his cousin, Anthony Johns, and the last third to John Bohemia of Redruth. Thomas Rosewarne, who remained as agent, reported to Mrs Moore.

Hugh Marriott had also died and in 1756

Aerial view of Grinton How Smelt Mill Peathouse and Flue (YDNPA)

Rosewarne began letting ground at Whitaside, Harkerside and Grovebeck to partnerships, many with partners in common. This led to a major rise in output, but meant that the mines were dominated by a few men.

The adventurers were encouraged to sink deeper shafts, to the Underset beds, by promises of time extensions to their grants. Hushing was also allowed, but at Grovebeck, at least, it was restricted to the time between Michaelmas and the end of March.

This prosperity brought with it another dispute, after a crosscut from one of John Harker and partners' five shafts at Whitaside, east of Greenhills Mine, found a new vein. In the hope of emulating their success, Richard Lonsdale took 10 meers immediately to the east of them. Not content with this, however, he began sinking shafts in Harker's ground, one of them only eight yards from the main shaft. After giving a warning to stop, which was ignored, Rosewarne was forced to pull down the windlass at the top of Lonsdale's shaft. After a brief pause, Lonsdale sank another shaft in Harker's ground and was again told to stop and the shaft head was destroyed. At this point, he seems to have sold some or all of his share and Henry Birkbeck took charge. From April 1763 the shaft was worked day and night, despite another discharge, until stopped by a Court Injunction

his widow, Lydia, sold the Grinton estate, including the smelt mill, to Caleb Readshaw of Richmond. He was an Alderman and had extensive interests in lead mines in Swaledale, Wharfedale and Southern Scotland. He was also a partner in a copper mine at Middleton Tyas.

Mrs Moore rented the How Smelt Mill from Caleb Readshaw and charged her lessees three shillings per fother (22 cwt), or a little over 13 pence per ton, for smelting there. Readshaw also supplied peat, as well as coal from his Grinton Moor Colliery, for use in the mill's ore-hearth.

Mining had been centred on the How, but from 1761

Grinton How Smelt Mill (L.O. Tyson)

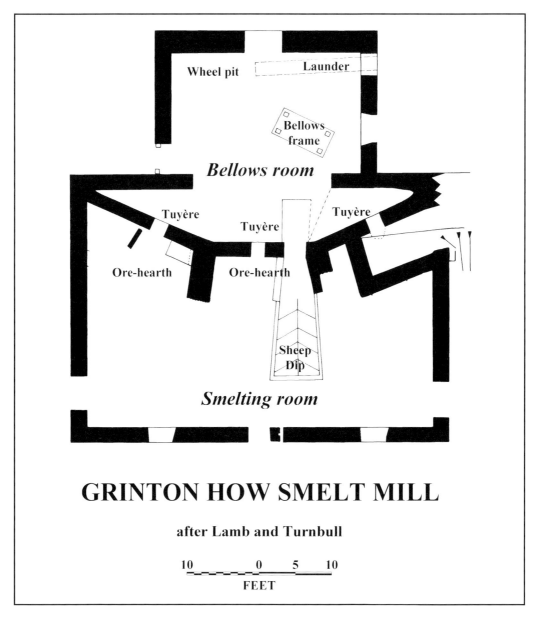

GRINTON HOW SMELT MILL

after Lamb and Turnbull

10   0   5   10

FEET

on February 9th 1764. During this period he raised £500's worth of ore.

The matter finally came before York Assizes in June 1764 and the points to be tried were agreed. These were whether Lonsdale's actions had been immediately or consequentially injurious to Harker and company, and also, whether or not the 'take notes' issued by Rosewarne were legally binding as they were on unstamped paper.

The matter had still not been settled in 1767, by which time many of the participants were dead, and it is not known if the matter was ever resolved.

Frances Moore died in May 1765 and her one-third share of the Grinton Mines was inherited by her niece, Elizabeth Knighton, wife of William Knighton of Beerferris in Devon. Anthony Johns still had his one-third, and Jane, the daughter of John Bohemia, and her husband, William Hambly, had the other third. As the lease was due to expire in 1774, they agreed that William Knighton should seek a new one from the Lords of the Treasury. An examination of the mines' fortunes under Edmund Moore revealed that, since September 1763, the lessees' losses over eight years amounted to £740 7s 10d, while profits over six years were £849 13s 2d and the Crown had got £106 4s 0d in royalties.

A delay in granting the new lease allowed others to make applications, too. One, from a neighbouring mine adventurer called Chauncy Townsend, included a proposal to drive a level which would drain his Apedale Mine. Another application came from Lord Bolton, who owned many mines on the north side of Wensleydale, including Apedale.

The delay also gave the partners time to fall out. Anthony Johns and William Hambly brought an unsuccessful claim against William Knighton, claiming that he had not paid them their proper share. Afterwards, Anthony Johns sold his share to Richard Turner of Tavistock, who was Knighton's solicitor, and William Hambly sold his to Caleb Readshaw.

Readshaw, Knighton and Turner then applied for a new lease, in 1774, asking for a reduction in duty from 1/5th to 1/8th because the mines were poor. This was confirmed in a report on the mines, commissioned by the Crown, in 1775. James Stodart & Company were working Harkerside Mine with 20 people, but were only covering their costs. Fowler, Hickes & Company employed around 30 men, women and children at the Grovebeck Mines and they too were only just covering their costs. Thomas Simpson & Company, with about 80 people at Whitaside Mine, had spent about £700 on trials, but only raised £300's worth of ore. The Crown granted a 31 year lease from December 1776, but only reduced the rate of duty to the, then quite liberal rate, of 1/7th.

In 1791, the manor of Grinton was sold to James Fenton, a West Yorkshire colliery owner, who built Grinton Lodge. His son, William Carr Fenton, sold the estate to Godfrey Wentworth, of Woolley, in 1839, but none of them appear to have been interested in the lead mines. William Knighton died before 1796 and half his share was taken by his son, John Moore Knighton of Grenosen in Devon. Knighton's daughters got a quarter of his share to divide between them and his wife got a full quarter. Caleb Readshaw Morley died in 1797 and his son, Josias Readshaw Morley of Beamsley Hall, got his share. John Moore Knighton also sold half his share to Morley. The new owners applied for a renewed lease with a reduction in duty to 1/8th, which was granted.

In 1817, the Grinton lessees, who called themselves the Grinton Moor Company, were:

	Share
Josias Morley	1/4
Mary Knighton	1/4
Mr Drake	
Mary Knighton's son-in-law	1/6
Mr Garden do	1/6
Mr Chadwick do	1/6

They sought a reduction in duty, claiming that the veins were exhausted in the Bearing Beds and that new, deeper and, therefore, expensive trials were needed. Only Whitaside and Summer Lodge Mines were producing ore and no trials were in progress. The Crown offered to reduce the duty to 1/10th, but reserved the old rate of 1/8th for Harker Vein, Birks, Brownagill, Harker End, Grove Beck and Grinton How, which the lessees claimed were worked out and abandoned for up to 100 yards on either side.

Josias Morley died in 1827, leaving his son and heir, Francis, with debts of around £26,000. The 1802 lease was due to expire in 1833 and, during negotiations for a new one, we learn that the mines employed over 200 men and that seven horse levels had been driven. The smelt mill had also been completely rebuilt in 1820. Summer Lodge was poorer, however, and the other mines were barely covering costs. John Harland, as agent to the principal partner, Francis Morley, managed the mines at Hurst as well as at Grinton.

The lease was renewed, but things did not

Grinton How smelt mill timber frame for the bellows (YDNPA)

to be deeply in debt. Morley's family repaid John Harland's efforts in clearing the earlier debt by claiming that he cheated them of £13,000, which Josias Morley left to his children in his will. Harland had been an assignee of Francis Morley's debts since 1848 and the court found that £3000 was outstanding. Harland refused to pay and the court sequestered his shares. Morley's shares were then sold at a public auction, held at the Buck Inn at Reeth on February 6th 1857.

The three companies continued working the mines in the 1860s. The Grinton Moor Company had the area around Devis Hole Level, and when the Kinnaird Commission visited Reeth in March 1863, its agent, George A. Robinson, had recently taken over. The miners at Devis had broken into a large system of natural caverns in the Main Limestone which penetrated nearly a quarter of a mile into the Ellerton liberty. Because most of the ore bearing beds had dipped below the drainage level, however, it was decided to drive a new and much deeper level from Cogden Gill. A branch of this level could also be used to drain the How Mines.

The company working Whitaside Mine was:-

	Share
John Barker	1/8
Thomas Smurthwaite	1/8
John Richard McCollah	1/8
James Robinson Tomlin	1/8
Ralph Milner	1/8
Edmund Coates	1/8
Isaac Fisher (representatives of)	1/8
Francis Garth	1/16
George Alderson (representatives of)	1/16

improve. By 1850, Smithy Level, at Whitaside, had got beyond the '*Old Man*' and found some ore in the Undersets, but the other mines were very poor, and the New Vein at Swinston Brow had been lost. It emerged that the proprietors had lost nearly £4000 since the lease was granted in 1833, and that Mrs Chadwick, who held her late husband's share, had been declared insolvent. In 1851, therefore, the partners sold their shares, for £150 each, to Isaac Fisher, Thomas Smurthwaite, James Robinson Tomlin and James Brown Simpson, all from Richmond, and Ralph Milner, of Reeth.

The above men, headed by Francis Morley, plus John Harland, took on yet another lease in 1853, but split the mine into three parts. They were part of a group which virtually monopolised lead mining in Swaledale, but would prove unable to make the Grinton Mines profitable again. Francis Morley died in 1854 and, like his father, Josias, was found

Its agent was Adam Barker, a descendent of the Adam Barker who managed Lord Wharton's mines at the end of the 17th century, and they had driven a new level for nearly 300 fathoms on a barren vein.

In 1855, the Wentworths sold their Grinton estate to another coal owner, Joseph Charlesworth, from Wakefield. He was principally interested in the area's grouse

Building at the mouth of Smithy Level, Whitaside

shooting, but also took an interest in the mines. When the Crown decided to sell its mineral rights at Grinton in 1876, Charlesworth paid £4000 for them.

The mines drifted on during the 1870s and into the 1880s, but were very poor. An improvement in the price of lead in the late 1880s encouraged the formation of new lead mining companies. Grinton was no exception and in October 1887 the Swaledale Mining Association Ltd was formed and began work at Whitaside in November.

In April the following year, the Grinton Mining and Smelting Company Limited was formed to take over the Association's rights. This was claimed to be a way of raising more capital, but it was also a way of buying out, often at inflated prices, the founders. Charlesworth and his wife held 700 shares, making them the principal shareholders.

Despite optimistic reports in the press, the company only ever worked in a small way, smelting 102 tons of lead between 1890 and 1892. The mine was standing in 1894 and the company was wound up in December 1895, bringing an end to mining at Grinton.

GRINTON MOOR MINE

Wellington Vein had been proved across the heads of Devis Hole and Glead Gills as far as the Ellerton boundary by a series of whim shafts in the late 18th century. By the early 1820s, however, a level was needed to drain the workings. This was Devis Hole Level, which was driven by Robinson, Whitelock & Company from Devis Hole Gill, a little upstream from its junction with Glead Gill. The level cut a series of caverns near the top of the Main Limestone, which greatly reduced the cost of driving it. Much of the ore was found in flots associated with Robinson's and Cranehaw Veins, but they were below the level and so the ore had to be hauled up sumps. This made it expensive to work and so in 1861, a deep level was begun from Cogden Gill. However, it was given up after 250 yards, long before it did any good.

John Rodwell, the Grinton Mining and Smelting Company's agent, began reopening Devis Hole Level in 1888 and formed a plan to drain a large, water-logged area of Ten Fathom Grit, called the "Swelly". To do this meant extending a crosscut from Haggs Gill Level, in the Ellerton liberty, and driving on Robinson Vein, from Devis. The two would then be linked by a 105 feet deep sump from the latter.

Six men were working day and night to enlarge an old drift running south-east on Robinson's Vein. Meanwhile, Haggs Gill Level had been cleared as far as Redway Head Vein by October 1888 and was being driven through broken ground towards the Grinton boundary. The forehead was only 42 feet from Robinson's Vein in February 1889 and in March it cut a fault, from which water flowed, and was directly under the drift from Devis Level. A rise from this place, begun in May, found the grit and a strong flow of water after 10 fathoms. The company also began repairing the old sumps and under levels in preparation for the water level falling. They were in ore-bearing ground by January 1889 and in March cut Close's Flot. A sump from the latter met water at a depth of 14 feet, however, and work stopped until the swelly was drained. Unfortunately, the mine appears to have closed before this was done.

GRINTON HOW MINE

This mine was on the hillside west from Lemon and Devis Hole Gills. How Vein crosses the Grinton to Redmire road, running from north-east to south-west, where it is in the Main Limestone. Blenk's and Ridley's hushes, dating from the 1750s, can be seen to the east of the road. How Level was driven south-west from the foot of Blenk's and Ridley's hushes, probably in the 1820s. It was worked until 1867, but for its last years the men were only gleaning ore left by the '*Old Man's*' shafts. Cooper's Level, which begins nearby and shares the same tip, tried the North Vein, but had little success.

Swinston Brow Level was driven from further down the hill to try How Vein in the Underset Limestone. It was abandoned around 1850, however, after the vein was found to split up and become barren.

On the west side of the road, the hillocks from shafts on How Vein and the North Rake, a branch from the former, can be seen. The ground between the veins carried flots in the chert bed above the Main Limestone. Most

of the shafts date from the 18th century, but Humphrey Wharton and Henry, Lord Scrope worked here in the early 17th century. It is also the scene of Thomas, Lord Wharton's trespass amongst Reginald Marriott's works in 1705.

HOW SMELT MILL

Previous histories of this mill, which was built by Reginald Marriott between 1710 and 1722, have been confused. For example, it was once believed to have had associations with the London Lead Company, but, as shown above, this was not so. It was also said to have been fitted with reverberatory furnaces and to have had a blowing machine, as opposed to bellows, but that was also wrong.

It was substantially rebuilt between 1820 and 1822, when the flue was apparently added. The latter had reached its full length of 1000 feet by 1854 and ended at a chimney on Sharrow Hill.

The Grinton Mining and Smelting Company Limited updated the mill in 1890 and put in a new ore-hearth, slag-hearth and roasting furnace, and repaired the flue. This company closed the mill when it gave up the mines in 1893.

The mill, which is the best preserved in the area, is a T-shaped building, comprised of a furnace house and a bellows house. The former, although altered when a sheep dip was built, still has three tuyère holes in the north wall, which indicate the position of the three hearths. Enough remains of the western hearth to give an impression of its complete form, which was an arched alcove. In the bellows house is a wooden framework which held the bellows, used for blowing the hearths. Air pipes led from these to the tuyères at the back of the ore- and slag-hearths. High in the north-east corner, the place where the launder entered the building, directly over the waterwheel, can be seen.

Other features on the site include a peat store, a horizontal flue, the foundations of

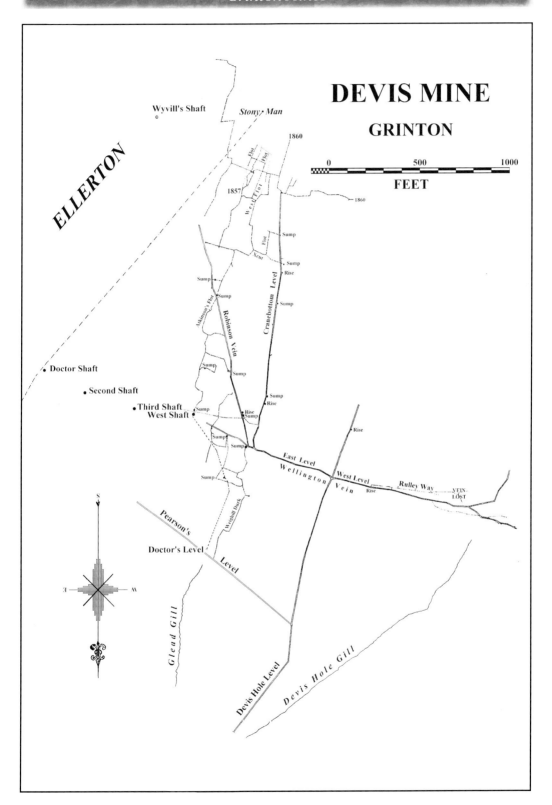

DEVIS MINE

GRINTON

two rectangular buildings, trackways and the water management system (dams, leats etc). In order to make space around the mill, the stream has been culverted under the site.

After closure, the buildings were used by the farmer, who stored hay and sheltered sheep in the peat house. He also built a sheep dip in the mill building. By the 1970s, however, the buildings were getting in need of repair. They were 'Listed' in 1973 and designated a scheduled ancient monument in 1975. This status, and an agreement with the mill's owner, allowed a series of conservation works to be done by the Yorkshire Dales National Park Authority between the late 1970s and the early 1990s.

GROVEBECK MINE

This mine worked a vein in the Main and Underset Limestones at the head of Grovebeck Gill. The vein was hushed and worked from a series of shafts in the 18th century, although the name Grovebeck, meaning Mine Beck, suggests mediæval mining there. In the 1760s, the vein and its surrounding ground was split into a number of blocks and let to partnerships.

Thomas Dunn and partners began sinking a shaft at the end of 1761 and, after five fathoms, found a rich flot in the Red Beds Limestone. By November 1768 they had raised 1422Ω tons of ore, but, although some eight or nine tons of ore were still being got each week, the flot was nearing exhaustion. Also in 1768, James Simpson was trying to find an Underset bed at Lower Grovebeck.

In the early 19th century, probably around 1819, Davis's Level was driven at the top of the Main Limestone. It is likely that Grovebeck Horse Level was driven at the bottom of the Main Limestone by Robinson, Whitelock & Company in the 1820s. Little ore appears to have been found at the latter horizon, but the level drained the old shafts and sumps westwards from Bowes Shaft. The vein was also worked in the Underset Limestone from sumps. By the 1850s the mine

was being worked sporadically by a small number of men, who were probably getting odd pockets of ore left by the 'Old Man'.

The Grinton Mining and Smelting Company was clearing Grovebeck Horse Level by September 1888, but after much work found that the mine had been cleaned out.

GROVEBECK MILL

This mill was probably built by Mrs Moore, soon after the discovery of Grovebeck Vein in 1762, and meant that, apart from the convenience of having a mill near their mines, the sub-lessees would not have had to pay Mrs Moore for smelting at the How Mill.

The layout of the mill is no longer obvious, as it has been totally levelled, but information from maps suggests that it was an oblong building, aligned nearly north to south, with a waterwheel on the outside wall of the south-west quarter. The water supply came from springs at the base of Long Scar and was carried in a leat to a reservoir, formed by an earth embankment which runs along the hillside. Water left the reservoir and ran down the hill in a spillway, before being led into another leat which ran along the hillside until it was above the mill. It then turned sharply and ran downhill to the start of the launder which fed the wheel. The waterwheel's tail water could either run back into the beck or be turned into the leat feeding the New Mill. It is unclear how long Grovebeck Mill lasted, but it probably closed around 1780, when output at Grovebeck was falling.

NEW MILL

This mill stood 1800 feet downstream of the Grovebeck Mill. Although not shown on Jackson's 1768 map, it was used by Mrs Moore, whose lease expired in 1774. It is likely, therefore, that New Mill was built between 1768 and 1770, when a rich strike was made. It is not referred to in documentation, but probably closed around 1800. It is shown as a ruin on the 1857 Ordnance Survey sheet.

The leat to the New Mill could take water either from Grovebeck or from the tail race of Grovebeck Mill. It fed a reservoir on the hillside above the mill, and this was supplemented with water from nearby springs.

The general size and shape of the mill building can be estimated from fragments of wall in the rubble. It was an oblong, of about 52 feet by 19 feet, and there are two, what appear to be, ore-hearth keeper stones, one at either end of the mill. There appears to be a second building, perhaps a slag crushing mill, downhill from the mill. There are scatters of slag between the two buildings and around the lower one.

SCOTT'S MILL

This mill was built by John Scott, a partner in the Beldi Hill Mine and one of those ejected from Spout Gill Mill in 1769 following a dispute with Lord Pomfret. Scott was also a partner, with Robert Elliott, in 10 meers of ground on Grovebeck. Faced with the loss of smelting facilities in 1769, it is likely that Scott built his mill around 1770.

As with the other two mills on Grovebeck, there are few references to Scott's Mill. During the rebuilding of the How Mill, between 1820 and 1822, some of its ore was smelted at Scott's Mill, when it was referred to as Grovebeck Mill. After that date, however, it is hard to see what ore it smelted, although some probably came from Ellerton, which by then had no mill of its own. Some confirmation of this came in March 1854, when John Bailey Langhorne of Reeth sold the mill to Marmaduke Wyvill, who was working at Ellerton. The sale included a *"Smelting Mill, Roasting Mill, Waterwheel, Billowes, Lobbys, buildings and water courses"*.

The Wyvill family gave up the Ellerton Mines in 1866, when the mill was also smelting ore from Whitaside Mine. It is likely that it closed very soon afterwards because

the Grinton and Ellerton Mines were then worked in common and ore would have been smelted at the How Mill. It is interesting to note that, despite working so late, the mill never had a flue, and this is possibly because the Lord of the Manor, who owned the land, would not allow one to be built. It may also be that, as the mill only smelted small parcels of ore, there was insufficient income to pay for a flue and the rebuilding that would have been necessary.

A leat took water from Grovebeck, near the New Mill tailrace, to a reservoir on the hillside above the mill. A further leat then ran north-east for a few yards before turning towards the mill. The spillway, where a launder also took water for the mill wheel, can still be seen.

Except for some grassy heaps and scatters of slags, little remains at this site. There are, however, some iron stays which once supported a roasting furnace.

HARKERSIDE MINES

The Harker Vein has been worked by hushing for over half a mile. An interesting 'pollution' effect, arising from this work, can be seen from across the valley. Enough calcarious material from the Main Limestone has been washed across the acid soils to cover the sandstone and shale beds and modify the types of plants growing in the affected areas. This shows up as a slightly greener 'tide mark'.

Harkerside prospered in the 17th century when, in 1650, it was valued at £20 per annum, which was only £2 less than Whitaside. Solomon Swale mined here too.

A level, which may date from Reginald Marriott's time, was driven south-south-east from the hush towards Grovebeck and was mentioned in a grant to Robert Elliott and partners in 1761.

The ground to the south of Harker Vein was tried by a 200 yard long hand level, driven west from near the eastern end of the hush, between 1861 and 1862. It found

Waterwheel pit for the crusher near Bradbury's and Smithy Levels, at Whitaside Mine (A. Winrow)

"flotty ground", but any ore had been got by the *'Old Man'*.

BROWNAGILL MINES

Little is known of these small mines, where a little ore was got from flots, but the Parke brothers were working there in the 1760s.

In 1822 and 1824, James Littlefair surveyed the workings from the 3rd shaft at Brown Gill, which belonged to G. Kay and William Hunter, and was leased from Messrs Knighton and Morley. Here, a crosscut, driven northwards from the shaft foot on top of the Main Limestone, got into a weak flot. Thomas Hunter had three pickmen at work here in 1830.

A level, driven from near the shooting hut, is mentioned in 1840 and a little ore was raised between 1862 and 1865.

WHITASIDE MINE

The principal veins here are Mason Rake, Whitaside Vein (which crosses into Apedale) and the Virgin String. The strings which cross Far Greena Hill and have been worked from shallow opencasts in the Main Limestone, are believed to be where Christopher Conyers was working in the early 16th century. Scatters of dressing waste and bales have been found nearby.

Mason Rake was worked in the 3rd Limestone, from a series of shafts, where it crosses Birks West Pasture. These workings were rich in the later 18th century. On the moor, Green Hill Mine worked flots associated with Mason Rake in the Main Limestone.

Whitaside Vein runs south-east and crosses into Wensleydale, where it was worked at Apedale Head. The early workings were in the area from which Smithy Level was driven and it was not followed southwards until 1761. The vein splits at the head of Ashpot Gutters, and Musgrave Flot was found between the branches. More flots and strings, between Whitaside Vein and Virgin String, were worked from shafts. The workings were so rich that 400 people were said to be working there in 1768. By 1775, however, this was down to 80. The vein was developed at depth from whim shafts, but from the late 1790s produced only enough ore to cover costs.

Smithy Level was driven by the Whitaside Company in the 1840s to drain the old workings and give easier access to the Underset Limestone. For a time the latter was productive, but it was found that the 'Old Man' workings were up to 30 or 40 yards deeper than Smithy Level. After a period of poverty, a sump from Smithy Level to the Underset Chert found payable ore in 1865. This was raised by a windlass and covered the mine's costs for the next two years. In time, however, the vein split up and became too expensive to work.

In the 1850s, the Low Level was driven both to prove and to drain Whitaside Vein in the Underset Limestone. It cut two veins and followed them, but the 'Old Man' had reached that depth, probably from Lonsdale's Whim. The Low Level was ventilated by a rise to Smithy Level, and a 20 fathom deep sump probably reached the 3rd Limestone, which was barren.

The mine closed in the 1870s, but was briefly reopened by the Grinton Mining and Smelting Company Limited in 1888, when an attempt was made to mine barytes.

SUMMER LODGE MINE

In the 1770s, interest spread to the Summer Lodge area, near the boundary with Lord Pomfret's mines at Spout Gill where a rich vein had been found. In February 1774, two brothers, Joseph and Thomas Cowling, each got Take Notes to try for ore at Summer Lodge. Thomas, with 10 meers of ground, found Summer Lodge Vein, and Joseph, with 8 meers, found an extension of Crackpot Moor Vein, which he called Cowling Rake. After two years, Joseph asked for a 21 year lease, but the Crown agents, despite having issued the Take Notes, said it was not Crown land.

Not surprisingly, Lord Pomfret laid claim to the area being worked by Cowling, but it was 1812 before the issue was pushed. In the meantime, a partnership, headed by Josias Readshaw Morley, began trying Summer Lodge thoroughly in 1808. When they found Summer Lodge Vein at Middle Tongue and began raising ore, John Davies, agent to the AD Lessors, protested. Nevertheless, it was not until March 1812 that Davies, acting on the orders of Peter Denys, had a trench dug in the disputed area.

The two sides prepared for a legal case, but Denys seems to have realised that their claim was weak because nothing came of it. As Tyson explained, "It is, however, more likely that ore production declined sharply after the initial bonanza".

Around 1817 the mine was leased to Messrs Raisbeck, Metcalfe & Company, at 1/6th duty. The early mining had been from shafts, but a level was driven from the stream side below the smelt mill. A line of bouse teams stands near its entrance.

After a period of idleness, the mine reopened in 1858 and by 1861 four men were driving a 100 fathom long level. By 1867, this level had cut a two foot wide vein carrying ore which was mixed with the gangue. In order to dress this, a grinding mill was built, but the mine closed soon afterwards.

SUMMER LODGE SMELT MILL

This mill, the most westerly of those in Grinton, served Summer Lodge Mine. Output rose rapidly in 1810 and the mill, which is shown on a map of March 1812, probably began smelting in 1811. Nearly 3000 tons of lead were made between then and 1817. It also smelted Grinton ore from 1820 to 1822, when the How Mill was being rebuilt. In addition to the mill, two miles of road were built by Josias Readshaw Morley and Company at a cost of between £700 and £800.

Summer Lodge Mill belonged to the Whitaside Mining Company in 1854, when the O.S. sheet was surveyed, and was apparently working. The latter company gave up in 1857, however, and the mines stood until 1862, when the Summer Lodge Mining Company (1862-1867) was formed. It is possible that the mill smelted then, but it was very outdated and, when Charlesworth bought the mining plant in 1876, it was not mentioned.

Ellerton and Stainton Mines

The minerals at Ellerton were owned by the Drax family, but they were often worked by people who also had mines at Grinton.

ELLERTON MOOR

A major fault, called the Great Stork Vein, runs from north-west to south-east and has thrown down the Main Limestone on its north side, thus dividing Ellerton Moor into two blocks. To the south, the Main Limestone outcrops much higher up the hillside.

A bale found on Ellerton Moor is evidence for mediæval mining there, but the earliest documented evidence is the discovery of Great Stork Vein in the adjoining Stainton liberty by its owner, Simon Scrope, in the late 17th century. Scrope got a lease from the Drax family and worked both mines until 1714, when Henry Drax recovered his mine because the lease had lapsed.

In 1754 a partnership of local men leased some of the mines, and in the following year William Sutton leased part of the mines and the smelt mill. He sold his share to one of the Parke brothers, with a payment of £5 19s 0d in 1768 and another of £3 1s 10d in 1769.

A number of flots on the Great Stork Vein, near the junction with East End Vein, were worked from shafts in the 18th century. These workings were drained by East End Level in the early 19th century. Around the same time, Derbyshire Level was driven in the 10 Fathom Grit, between the Crow and Red Beds, to try the eastern end of Great Stork Vein.

On the south side of Great Stork Vein, Haggs and Redway Head Veins, which run south into Wensleydale, were worked from shafts in the 18th century. The principal workings, however, were on Wellington Vein, which was also worked from Devis Hole Level in Grinton. Most of the ore came from flots and this is reflected in the fluctuating output. In 1810, for example, William Chaytor claimed that Ellerton was the richest mine in the country, but by 1818 output was very low. In the 1820s the Grinton Moor Company drove Haggs Gill Level south-west on Wellington Vein at such a depth that, when it crossed Great Stork Vein, it entered the 27 Fathom Grit and was well placed to try the Underset Limestone. The level was probably planned by John Harland and followed the vein almost up to the Grinton boundary.

In 1827 John Sawbridge married Jane Drax, owner of the Ellerton Mines, and soon discovered that the Grinton Moor Company had been working them without a lease. He began proceedings to eject them, but, by the time an injunction was issued, John Harland, Josias Morley's executor, had exhausted the mines.

Marmaduke Wyvill leased the mines around 1836, by which time Haggs Gill Level was well advanced. As there was no longer a smelt mill in Ellerton, Wyvill bought Scott's mill, on Grovebeck, in 1845. He sank Wyvill's Whim on Peacock's Vein and by 1854 he was working Cooper's and Peacock's Shafts, in the Red Beds Limestone. Owing to the mine's poverty, however, the miners were confined to the old workings. When it was given up in 1866, the Wyvills had lost thousands of pounds.

The Ellerton Mines were worked in common with Grinton from 1870, when a crosscut was driven from the end of Haggs Gill Level towards Robinson's Vein. The forehead was still 38 fathoms short of its objective in the grit under the Main Limestone, when the mines closed in 1875. The crosscut was resumed by the Grinton Mining and Smelting Company Limited in 1888. It cut Robinson's Vein in 1890, when some *"nice ore"* was found in a nearby cross vein, but the *'Old Man'* had got most of the ore in the Main Limestone. Unfortunately, the Underset Limestone was below Haggs Gill Level at this point and any ore was under water, making it expensive to work, and so the mine closed.

Ellerton Smelt Mill stood near the ford over the Swale on the track to Marrick. No date has been found for it being built, but Lord Wharton sent ore there in the early 1680s, when it had an ore-hearth and a slag hearth.

The mill was leased to Henry Sutton and Ralph Hutchinson, along with the Ellerton Mines, in 1754, when they paid £38 11s 6d for the smelting tools etc. It is shown on Jackson's 1768 map of the area, but is not on maps dating from the 1820s. It is likely, therefore, that the mill closed in the late 18th century when the Ellerton Mines were worked in common with those on Grinton Moor. Except for some grassy hillocks, there are few obvious remains of the mill.

STAINTON MOOR

After Old Stork Vein leaves Ellerton Moor it runs east across Stainton Moor, which was owned by the Scropes of Danby. The vein, which was worked by shallow shafts from the late 18th century, has also been opencast near the boundary. Until 1786, when Scrope built his own smelt mill in Stainton Gill, the ore was smelted at Clints in Marske, or Preston Mill near Keld Heads, or Braithwaite Mill in West Burton. Scrope's mill was small and probably only had one ore-hearth. It is shown on Greenwood's map of 1817, but it is not marked on the first edition of the Ordnance Survey map.

William Chaytor was working the mine in the early 19th century, when Dagget's and Wyvill's Levels were driven to try the vein at depth. The last attempt to mine lead came in April 1880, when the Stainton Moor Lead Mining Company Ltd was registered. Little, if any, work was done however, and the company was wound up in 1882.

Hurst Mines

In the early 12th century the manor of Marrick was granted to Roger Aske in return for Knight Service to Earl Conan at Richmond castle. Around 1165, Roger's grandson, also called Roger, founded a priory for Benedictine nuns on the north bank of the Swale near Marrick. The nuns were given land and a tithe of the lead ore to support their activities. The priory was built using stone quarried at Awkmay Craggs, Roanmire and Skegdale. The roofs were covered with lead from local mines, which had been worked *"from time out of minde"* at Copperthwaite, Blakey How, Redd Hurst, Grenehowse and Ullandes Barf.

William, the last of the Aske male line, died in 1512 and the Marrick estate passed to his two daughters. When one of them died in 1535, the estate was reunited in the hands of Sir Ralph Bulmer, the other daughter's husband. He granted meers on the above veins to partnerships of miners and local gentry in return for a duty of one third or one fourth part, plus a one-ninth part, called lott.

The next 100 years, or so, saw the manor of Marrick divided and change hands a number of times and what follows is a very simplified version of those events. Under Henry VIII's dissolution of the monasteries, the prioress, Christabell Cowper, and the 16 nuns surrendered Marrick Priory to Leonard Beckwith and John Uvedale, as Crown commissioners, in November 1540. Using his position, Uvedale eventually got a 21 year lease of the priory and its lands. Then, in 1545, he bought Marrick Priory and its land from the Crown for £364 1s 0d. He also had a lease of lead mines on the former Byland Abbey's lands in Nidderdale. In 1549 John Uvedale was succeeded by his son, Avery, who was also important in public life.

Sir Ralph Bulmer, the owner of the rest of Marrick, died in 1554 and his estate passed to his son-in-law, John Sayer, of Worsall near Yarm. He held his part of Marrick until 1618 when he gave it to his brother's daughter and her new husband William Bulmer. The latter was the great-nephew of Sir Ralph Bulmer and so the estate returned to the Bulmer family which had held it until 1554.

When Avery Uvedale died in June 1583, he left the Marrick Estate to his eldest son, John. Five years later, John sold it for 200 marks to Richard Brakenbury of Sellaby, Co. Durham. Brakenbury, who also had the neighbouring Ellerton Priory, sold Marrick Priory and its lands to Sir Timothy Hutton of Bishop Auckland in March 1592. He then leased them to Robert Blackburne, a London upholsterer, for 21 years at an annual rent of £149 9s 5d, in 1596. Four years later Sir Timothy's father, Mathew Hutton, bought the adjoining manor of Marske for £3000 and left it to Sir Timothy when he died in 1601.

Meanwhile, Sir Timothy Hutton had got into debt and when he died in 1629, his son, Mathew, sold the Priory estate, including the lead tithes, to Robert Blackburne for £3800. Blackburne immediately brought an action at law against William Bulmer, alleging that he, his father, Sir Bertram, and John Sayer had occupied ground at Red Hurst from October 1630 to August 1631, and raised 80 tons of ore on which they had paid no tithes. This attempt to enforce payment of tithes on lead was being repeated elsewhere, particularly in Derbyshire, with widely varying success. The outcome of Blackburne's case is not known, but in 1634 he sold the tithes to William Bulmer for £750.

The Bulmers and Sayers were Catholics and, as the 17th century progressed, they became subject to fines levied on recusants. These fines caused William Bulmer to let the mines to Sir Thomas Tempest and Sir William Lambton, both of Co. Durham, on a 21 year lease in 1635 in return for their clearing his debt of £4938 arising from fines. Then in 1641 Bulmer sold the lead tithes to George Scott. Finally Bulmer's estate was sequestered in 1654 and Lady Troth Tempest, to whom the lease of the mines had descended, had to appeal to the Committee for Sequestrations to recover the mines and her part of the estate.

The Bulmer's debts had become so big that, in 1648, they were forced to transfer the rest of their Marrick holdings, including the lease, to Thomas Swinburne, a relative by marriage of the Bulmer and Tempest families. Their agreement was that Swinburne, who had also bought the lead ore tithes from George Scott in 1652, would let Bulmer repurchase the estate at some unspecified future date. When Bulmer sought to do this, however, Swinburne refused to sell.

Swinburne's affairs did not flourish, however, and so he sold the estate and mines to Charles Powlett, the son of the Marquis of Winchester, in 1668. Powlett, who was also able to buy out the Bulmer and Blackburne families' share of the manor in 1671 and 1683 respectively, was created Duke of Bolton in 1689. When he died, in 1699, his Marrick estate passed to Lord William Powlett.

In August 1817, Josias Readshaw Morley, of Beamsley Hall near Skipton, bought the manor and mines of Marrick from the Powlett family. He was involved with other Swaledale mines, but was already in such debt that he had to sell an estate at Addingham, also near Skipton, to pay his way.

When Morley died in 1827, his debt-encumbered estates were inherited by his son, Francis, who came of age in 1834. His trustees sold the Beamsley estate and employed Captain John Harland, of Reeth, to manage the Marrick estate and mines. Thanks to Harland's efforts, a total debt of £26,000 was cleared.

THE MINES AND SMELT MILLS

The mines are centred on the hamlets of Hurst and Washfold, in the parish of Marrick. Here, the Yoredale strata dips gently eastwards from Fremington Edge, and much of the ore came from the beds of sandstone, chert and thin limestone above the Main Limestone. Where worked, however, the latter bed and the Underset Limestone and Chert were also productive. The absence of surface water restricted the use of waterwheels for pumping. This, and the gentle surface slopes at Hurst, also meant that hushing was only used near Nungate.

The Great Blackside Vein, itself a continuation of Fryerfold Vein, runs south-east through Slei Gill, in Arkengarthdale, and over Fremington Edge to become the Wellington, or Racca Vein at Hurst. On reaching Hind Rake, however, Racca Vein curves until it runs north-east and Hind Rake splits into a half-mile wide belt of veins and strings which were rich in lead ore. None of them continue beyond Wallnook Vein, however, which runs from north-west to south-east and intersects them.

South of the above, there are a small number of veins at Jingle Pot and Copperthwaite, which run almost east to west between Fremington Edge and the road to Hurst. Shaw Vein, which becomes Pryes Vein on crossing Shaw Beck, is nearly parallel to Wallnook Vein and was the only productive vein on the north-east side of it. A number of poor veins have also been tried in the area around the smelt mills and nearer Marrick.

The mines were extensive in monastic times, but they had probably been so for much

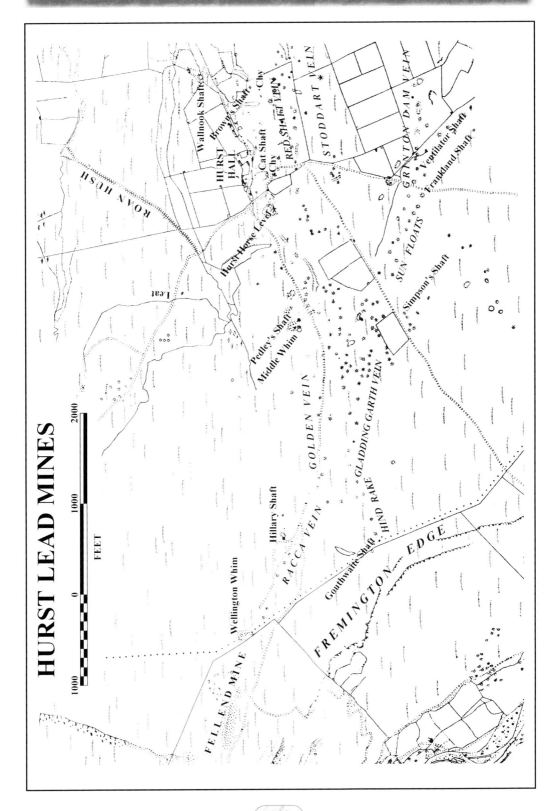

HURST LEAD MINES

An early view of Level Houses at Hurst

longer. The mediæval miners won their ore from myriad shallow shafts, especially on Hind Rake, and worked under a form of Customary Mining Law, which was similar to that used in other parts of Yorkshire and especially Derbyshire. This law is thought to date from the Anglo-Saxon period, but the earliest written example, from Derbyshire, dates from 1288. Although it was certainly widespread in Swaledale, the only known record of the laws there was quoted in a dispute of 1574:-

first when the mine is fownde of newe in the moores, the marchantes and miners shall chose theime a barghe master otherwise callide a moore master for to deliver to the finders of the mine ij meares under a stake, and oone meare to the lorde nexte unto the same finders

and afterwarde the moore master shall deliver the saide felde to the miners bi certaine meares to theime that will worke theime after the lawe of the mine

and after that the lorde of the fielde and the miners shall ordeine a coverable dishe bi the which the lordde shall receave his lotte and the miners there right of the mine

that is the miners eight dishes and the lorde the ninthe, and the chirche the tenthe

and the miners abiding and conversante apon the mine shall have sufficient howsebote and hedgebote and all maner of timber for theire groves, bi the deliverie of the lorde or his forrester, if he have sufficient within the lorde shippe

and if none maie be fownde within the lorde shippe, and thei be providid for timber at theire costes in other plasis out of the lorde shippe then the lorde shall nothing take for his lotte

hearre note that the lotte ure is given for timber wodde to be hadde to the groves and not for anie titell or right that the lorde hathe in the mine, more than a nother miner

which being plaine then the finders, and other that will worke be as free to have a meare of grownde as the lorde, if the moore master will so deliver it

and in this sortte the priores of marrigge, hadde all waies her meares of grownde deliverede to her in divers plasis apon the more of marrigge bi the more masters from time to time, as often as anie newe mine or fielde was fownde

Aerial view of heavily mined ground between Cat and Brown's Shafts at Hurst (YDNPA)

and the saide meares of grownde be yet knowen to this daie apon the moore of marrigge

as at coppthwate redde hirste ullandes barghe sele gill blokey howes and grenenose

and all thiese meares of grownde thei ever hadde severallie to theire owne usis

besides the tythe of everie meare of grownde that was wrought apon the moore

Some of these mining grants are recorded in wills. For example, in 1504 Christopher Conyers, owner of the manor of Marske, left *"William my son a more meer at Coupperthwaite, which I bought of Thomas Metcalfe"*.

Until 1574/5, ore from Hurst was carried to Fremington Edge, where it was smelted at four bales situated to the east of the trigonometrical station. The nuns also had some meers and raised from nine to ten tons of lead annually. Their ore was smelted at the priory's bale, which was to the east of the others. A plan, dated 1592, shows a line of four bales plus another, belonging to Marrick Priory, offset from them. The likely ownership of at least some of the other bales is suggested by Adam Spensley's evidence in a boundary dispute between Roger Aske and Christopher Conyers in 1502. Spensley related that *"he hath seen the Askes and Bulmers, owners of the manor of Marrick, cut down, carry away, and burn at their lead bales such wood as grew upon Hazelhow and Hawthorns"*. This shows that the Mineral Lords regulated the miners by controlling smelting, which was the general rule in Yorkshire, but not in Derbyshire.

The first known smelt mill in Swaledale was built by John Sayer, on the side of Dales Beck at Marrick, in 1574/5. He had inherited his share of the manor from his father-in-law, Sir Ralph Bulmer, in 1554. Water came to the mill, which was on the site of the present Low Smelt Mill, in a leat from higher up the course of Dales Beck. This tells us that it had waterwheel-powered bellows and an ore-hearth at a time when they were first being introduced to Derbyshire.

Sayer's Mill was called the Low Mill by 1660, when it had a slag-hearth and was smelting slags from Thomas Swinburne's High Mill. Between 1660 and 1663, the Low Mill also smelted 108 tons of bale slags:-

Horse loads of slags (= 2 cwts)	From
594	old smeltings
331	Fremington Edge
158	Skelton Moor

Accounts for the same period show that Thomas Hudson was paid 11s 8d *"for mending the Low Mill bellows and for mending the chimney and for putting* [in] *tridles and taps"*. The latter were made of thorn wood and were the pegs, fixed to the

waterwheel's axle, and the levers which they struck, thus transferring rotation into a reciprocating movement, to drive the bellows.

The slag-hearth burnt a crude form of coke, called cinders, made from local coal. This appears in the accounts as *"Paid Raife Maynard for leading 306 quarters of cinders and for burning them at Coal Pit Moor at 2s 6d per quarter"*.

The Low Mill had closed by 1705, when an agreement settling a dispute between Lord Powlett and John Hutton over the boundary between Marrick and Marske refers to only one mill. Thomas Jackson's 1782 map of the Marrick Estate shows the later High Mill, but does not name a small building on the site of the Low Mill.

Returning to the late 16th century, there was a great deal of animosity between the Uvedales, Bulmer and Sayer, because the first was a Protestant and the other two were Catholics. In 1580 Avery Uvedale complained to the Queen that, on November 20th, John Sayer had incited 20 local man who *"with*

Aerial view of Marrick's High and Low smelt mills and peat houses

great force and avarice and in riotous manner and strong hand, with staves, daggers, iron pikes and pyccals and other defensible weapons, have entered into a certain hill or burgh called Ullands hill", where they dug several shafts and trenches, spoiling the pasture and took away £20's worth of lead ore. The outcome is not known, but Uvedale urged that the case be dealt with quickly *"because they be a multitude and may do me bodily hurt"*.

By the early 1660s, the shafts at Red Hurst were troubled with water and so Thomas Swinburne, the new owner, began driving the

Copperthwaite in return for a salary of £51 13s 4d. Men on deadwork were paid on fathomtale. Typically, this was between 3s 6d and 4s 6d per fathom for shaft sinking, and around 2s 0d per fathom for driving crosscuts. As this was before the introduction of gunpowder blasting, there are also references to the use of fire setting for driving tunnels. This involved lighting fires against the rock, causing it to fracture and thus making it easier to work with picks and wedges. Although the method must have been widespread, references to its use in Yorkshire mines are rare. The men paid 6d per pound for their

Marrick High smelt mill, 1976

Low, or Old Water, Level from a natural sink hole near Washfold in order to drain them. The level was 3000 feet long by 1718 and was in the Main Chert, on top of the Main Limestone, for much of its length. It was the lowest drainage level in this part of the mine and any deeper working was from sumps or from a number of deep whim shafts.

Swinburne's agent, John Fawcett, oversaw miners working in shafts at Red Hurst and

candles. For getting ore, miners were paid on bingtale. This was between 17 and 18 shillings per bing of dressed ore, or an average of 43s 9d per ton. The dressing was done by the miners or their families.

Thomas Swinburne built the High Smelt Mill around 1660, to supplement Sayer's Mill, which then became known as the Low Mill. Water for the mills came from some springs in a leat, which fed three dams in

Smelting Mill Wood, alongside the lane leading to the mills. A few yards below the lowest dam are the remains of two peat houses. Both mills had waterwheel-powered bellows, and the tail water from the High Mill fed the Low Mill's waterwheel.

The High Mill is split into two rooms, with a central chimney. The bellows room, at the west end, has a waterwheel pit on its east to west axis. The wheel, which was about 21 feet in diameter by four feet wide, probably had bellows on either side of it, one pair for each hearth. The smelting room, which is 25 feet by 17 feet, has two ore-hearth arches opening into it. Fumes from the hearths were led into a chimney, directly above them, which has been extended twice.

The ore-hearth burnt chopwood, which was dried in a kiln near the mills. It came from a variety of places, including Mr Blackburne's woods at Marrick, Lamb Close, Downholme, Thorpe and Braithwaite, in Coverdale. The chopwood was supplemented with a little coal.

Part of the High Mill's roof was blown off by a gale in April 1661, when Thomas Hudson was paid for patching the hole with sods to keep the weather out. This temporary

Marrick High smelt mill, 1946

Marrick High and Low smelt mills

repair was later replaced with 150 roofing flags, costing 10 shillings, from Leonard Addison's quarry at Healaugh.

Lead from both the High and the Low Mills was carried to Hartforth, where it was stored on its way to Stockton. The carriers were paid between 6s 0d and 6s 8d per fother for this work.

No 18th century records of the mill are known, but it is unlikely that the structure was changed significantly. The High Smelt Mill was becoming inefficient by the late 1830s, when Jaques & Company built the new Low Mill and closed it.

Swinburne's affairs did not flourish, however, and in 32 months, the mines cost him £2559 9s 7d and produced lead worth £2678 10s 1d. The resulting profit, of £119 0s 6d. was only two per cent per year on his outlay. In order to clear his debts, therefore, Swinburne sold the estate and mines to Charles Powlett, the son of the Marquis of Winchester, in 1668. Powlett was also able to buy out the Bulmer and Blackburne families' share of the manor in 1671 and 1683 respectively.

Powlett, who was created Duke of Bolton in 1689, worked the mines, along with others at Grassington and Starbotton that he leased from the Earl of Burlington. When he died, in 1699, his Marrick estate passed to Lord William Powlett.

John Blackburne, who in 1683 had sold all his land at Marrick, save the site of the priory, to Charles Powlett, was a partner in a number of mining ventures. These included mines at Buckden, Kettlewell, Arncliffe, Appletreewick and a trial near Horton in Ribblesdale. He also formed a partnership, including Emmanuel Justice, Mr Langstaff, Ralph Rowlings and Reuben Orton and others, to build the third mill at Marrick, which was the Cupola Mill at Reels Head. They paid Thomas Buckton nine pounds for the land and began building towards the end of 1700. Smelting began in 1701 and John Blackburne's nephew, John Copperthwaite, was employed as manager.

Apart from earthworks and some low walls, little remains of this mill, which was a very important and innovative development. Cupolas, or reverberatory furnaces burnt coal on a separate fire grate and the heat was reflected onto the ore, which was in a low-arched compartment, by a brick fire-bridge. This kept the coal smoke away from the lead and allowed more ore to be smelted at once. Because they were built of fire brick and their temperature could be controlled, reverberatory furnaces could also work for much longer than ore-hearths, which had to be put out and allowed to cool. This gave savings in fuel, scale and the furnace's idle time.

The mill burnt coal from County Durham and from a pit in Burton Park, Wensleydale, in which John Blackburne had a share. It cost £1 5s 0d per fother to cart the ore from Buckden and the smelters were paid 11s 6d for every 22 cwt of lead they made. The lead was taken either to Stockton via Hartforth and then the River Tees, or to York by way of Boroughbridge and the River Ouse, where it was sold.

The first successful cupolas in Britain were used in the 1680s for lead and copper smelting near Bristol. Others, for lead, were built during the 1690s in Flintshire, where they were also later used by the London Lead Company at its Gadlys works. In 1735 they were introduced to Derbyshire where, by the 1780s, they superseded the ore-hearth. A few were also used in the north Pennines.

Marrick Cupola was the first in Yorkshire and it was not until 1792 that the next one was built at the Duke of Devonshire's Grassington mines. Recent work by archæologists has also suggested that the mill at Marrick had two short flues on the hillside behind it. If so, this is the first known use of flues at a British smelt mill. Previously, the oldest known flue was the one built in 1778 at the Upper Cupola in Middleton Dale, Derbyshire.

Unlike most other Yorkshire smelt mills, which served specific mines or liberties, the Cupola was a jobbing mill, which smelted parcels of ore brought from any mine. For example, in 1703 it smelted parcels of ore from Buckden Gavel Mine, Reginald Marriott's Grinton mines, Mr Thompson's 'new trial' on Woodhall Greets in Wensleydale, and Copperthwaite Vein near Hurst. Sometimes there were problems keeping the mill supplied with ore, however.

Justice and Blackburne were partners in the Blew Groves Mine, at Buckden, and, contrary to the terms of their lease, which stipulated that their ore was to be smelted at the Earl of Burlington's Grassington mill, they took it to the Cupola at Marrick. In 1704 a series of legal disputes broke out between them, when Blackburne discovered that Justice had cheated him over the partnership's finances. The cost of these disputes eventually meant that Blackburne lost his house at Fryerhead, near Malham, and that he had to mortgage the Marrick Priory estate. The disputes also meant the end of the Cupola Mill, which was in ruins by 1725 when it was demolished.

The mines prospered under Lord William Powlett and Hurst began to grow. His Steward, John Cotesworth, was installed at the newly built Hurst Hall. Some idea of the scale of the mines is given in June 1718, when a new company leased them for 21 years, at a duty of 1/7th payable in dressed ore, with the proviso that at least 147 miners were employed. This company was made up of:-

Samuel Mellor	
Gyrn, Flintshire	1/3 share
John Halsall	
St Dunstan's in West London	1/3 share
William Thompson	
Thames Street, London	1/6 share
Thomas Jones	
Pentreff, Flintshire	1/6 share

Their agent was to be Thomas Kinnersley, of Park Hall at Healaugh, at a salary of £40.

At this time, the extensive workings were centred on Golden Vein and drained into Swinburne's Low Water Level. They were served by 16 main shafts, between 12 and 24 fathoms deep.

The duty paid by this company is recorded until August 1727 and averaged 30 tons per year, which suggests an average output of around 210 tons. The company's lease should have run until November 1739, but nothing has been found about the years after 1727. Lord William Powlett died in 1729 and was succeeded by his son, who was also called William and who may have sought a new company. In June 1747 the Court of the London Lead Company proposed taking all his mines in Marrick on a 31 year lease, but nothing has been found to suggest that a lease was ever granted.

The mines were certainly worked vigorously during the rest of the 18th century and by 1782, when records start again, they were very extensive. Shaw Level had been driven to Wallnook Vein near Shaw, Copperthwaite Vein was being worked by Sun Hush and several deep shafts, Jingle Pot and Grinton Dam Veins were being worked from shafts, and Nungate Level was being driven on the Hurst veins.

Soon after buying the manor and mines in

Flues at the rear of Marrick Low smelt mill, 1946

August 1817, Josias Readshaw Morley began Hurst Horse Level to get into the Crow Beds at the western end of the veins and connect with Wellington Whim Shaft, which followed the vein into the Main Limestone and eventually linked with Fell End Level, driven from the Fremington side of the scar. The Middle Whim Shaft, near the centre of the field, worked Blindham, Golden and Cherry Veins in the beds above the Main Limestone.

When Morley died in 1827, his trustees employed Captain John Harland, of Reeth, to manage the mines. In January the following year, the mines were leased to Robert Jaques and Company, who also worked the Old Gang, Surrender, Arkengarthdale and Fremington Mines. John Harland took a one-eighth share in the new company. In addition to an annual rent of £800, they were to pay the then low rate of duty of 1/14th.

Bargains were made for hauling ore up the whim shafts with, for example, Mathew Peacock being paid 2s 6d per draught at the Middle Whim. This rate, which was usually for 100 kibbles, included the provision of horses to drive the whim. Once the ore was at the surface, carriers were paid to take it to the new dressing floor, with a waterwheel-powered grinding mill, which was built to serve Hurst Horse Level. Another grinding mill was built at the mouth of Fell End Horse Level, which was inside the Hurst boundary by November 1831.

The new company also prospected outlying veins, but had little success. Queen's Level, its major success, was begun in June 1837 and developed the veins in the 10 Fathom Grit, below the Crow Beds. Two crosscuts, one driven north from Queen's Level, worked Wellington and Golden Veins, and the other, driven south, worked Cleminson and Redshaft Veins. An under-level, called Brown's Rulley Way, was used to work in the Red Beds Limestone and the Main Chert.

As noted above, the High Smelt Mill was inefficient and so Jaques & Company needed a new mill to smelt their ore from Queen's Level. The site chosen for it was that of the Sayer's, or Low, Smelt Mill. It was built in the late 1830s and, as shown on the 1854 OS sheet, it had a short flue leading to a chimney on the hillside behind it. The High Mill was abandoned and by 1861, when the Hurst Mining Company took over, it was beyond repair.

In 1852 a market was found for dressed ore, which saved the cost of smelting it. By 1858, therefore, the Low Mill was seldom used and most of the ore was sold unsmelted. This lasted until 1862 when all the ore raised that year was smelted to give 111.70 tons of lead. Some old machinery, including a 20 foot diameter by 39 inch breast waterwheel, was bought from the Lane End Mines for £55 and preparations were made to install the wheel in the Low

Bridge at Pryes Mine, 1986

Mill during the winter of 1862-63. The flue was also extended to the High Mill, which was sealed and the old furnace room used as a settlement chamber, with the fume venting from its chimney. Interestingly, stone from the High Mill chimney was used to build part of the new flue. It seems likely, therefore, that the two extensions (one in brick, the other in stone) to the latter chimney were built in the 1860s, probably to improve the draught. A slag hearth and a new ore lobby were also added to the Low Mill.

This new arrangement was abandoned early in 1868 and the mines went back to selling unsmelted ore. Five tons of pig lead was sold in 1869, but this came from stock because it was from the last mark (letter T) smelted in early 1868. Another five tons was sold in 1871, and 0.2 ton in 1874. The latter parcel was probably made up of lead salvaged from around the mills.

Marrick High Smelt Mill is still almost complete to roof height and, as such, is the best preserved 17th century lead smelting mill in Britain, and possibly the world. The present Low Smelt Mill is also in reasonable repair and both mills are Scheduled Ancient Monuments. Until Les Tyson deduced the correct sequence of the three mills on this site, there had been some fanciful interpretations of their histories and relationship.

Francis Morley came of age in 1834 and in

Pryes Level

1842 he fell out with Jaques & Company over who should pay the income tax due on his duty lead. As a result, the company gave up the mines, and Morley, who had sacked John Harland, began working them himself. Like his father, Francis was soon in debt and was forced to rehire John Harland in order to work the mines profitably and begin clearing his debts. Despite Harland's best efforts, however, Francis Morley fled the country in 1848, to escape his creditors, and went to live with his uncle in Calais. Harland once more pacified the most vociferous creditors and rescheduled the debt repayments, thus allowing Morley to return.

Pryes Mine shop

Harland had no luck in finding a new company to work the mines and so he formed one himself in 1844 and, along with Mr Brown Simpson of Richmond, soon became a majority shareholder. They raised a moderate amount of ore, but high working costs denied them much profit. Morley, on the other hand, did well from his duty lead. Nevertheless, when Morley died in August 1854, Harland was replaced as the estate's agent by Christopher Lonsdale Bradley, who had the West Swaledale and Blakethwaite Mines.

Harland and Simpson kept on the mines, but, contrary to an agreement made in 1852, Bradley insisted that duty should be paid in smelted lead. Bradley also diverted estate timber from the Hurst Mines to others in which he had a share. Two new, major levels were begun. The first, called Porter Level, was driven south from Moresdale Beck and was 1380 feet long by 1861. The second was Pryes Level, which in 1859 was driven from the side of Shaw Beck. It was the deepest level at the mines and cut Pryes Vein in the Underset Limestone.

In 1859, George Chalder, who had been agent at Hurst for 66 years, died at the age of 87. The following year Harland and Simpson gave up the mines, and Francis Morley's son, who was also called Francis, agreed a 21 year lease with a new company which traded as the Hurst Mining Company. Its agent was Robert Daykin, from Arkengarthdale, and the partners were:-

Bouse teams at Pryes Mine

George Leeman
Solicitor
York

William Fox Clarke
York

Christopher Lonsdale Bradley
Richmond

Thomas Jackson
Eltham Park, Kent

Thomas Jackson Jnr
Eltham Park, Kent

Alfred William Bean
Shooters Hill, Kent

James Gow
Fowlers Park, Kent

When an inspector from a government commission visited Hurst in January 1863, some 67 pick men and a few women were employed on the dressing floors. The men were paid monthly and, as was usual, had deductions made to cover the cost of their blasting powder, tools, candles and drawing their work to surface (either up shafts or along the levels). The company bought candles for 5s 6d per dozen and sold them for 8s 0d per dozen.

Besides continuing the existing levels, three new ones had been started, each with four men. These were Marrick Moor and Marrick High and Low Levels. Thirty men were also stoping at Copperthwaite Level.

Most of the workings were ventilated naturally, by shafts and levels, but air was taken into dead-ends by air pipes. There were two fans, or 'Windy Kings'. One was driven by a small waterwheel and the other was turned by a boy. Air was carried from them to the workings in wooden trunks, or ducts, about six inches by four inches. At the time of the inspector's visit, the air in parts of Pryes Level was very bad because parts of the workings were flooded and the ventilation was stopped.

Pryes Level was then 1440 feet long and a sump, which eventually reached a depth of 45 fathoms, was being sunk from it to work a large ore-shoot in the beds between the Underset Limestone and the sandstone above the 4th Limestone. In order both to pump the water and to lift rock from this sump, the company installed one of William Whitham's water-pressure engines in the summer of 1864. The engine, which cost £500, was housed in an underground chamber, a little off and above the level.

Francis Morley, who had been away in the army, came home in 1866 and soon realised that Bradley had abused his position as agent for both the estate and the mining company. For example, there were serious discrepancies in his accounts. There had been unauthorized expenditure on the smelt mill, and Morley had been charged for smelting his duty lead when it should have been free of all charges. Bradley was sacked from his post as estate manager and replaced by H.T. Robinson, with William Waggett over seeing day-to-day business.

By June 1869 there was good ore in Pryes Engine Sump, if the water could be kept down, but Metcalfe, the company's agent, was of the opinion that a steam engine was needed because there was not enough water for the water-pressure engine both to pump the water and draw the work. No steam engine was bought, however, and a drought in the following summer meant that the sump, which was then the company's chief source of ore, could not be worked. As for many other lead mines, the 1870s were a time of

Brown's Engine shaft - chimney

crisis with slow demand and low prices. It was also a time when many of the long established owners of Yorkshire lead mines, who had kept out foreign interests, got out. The Hurst Mining Company did well to struggle on, but it is likely that Pryes Engine Sump was abandoned around 1876 when the mines' output began to fall. By 1880, the company was paying the dead rent and doing very little mining.

Faced with this apathy, Francis Morley granted a six-month exploration lease to Faithfull Cookson in April 1881. Cookson was a mining speculator with widespread interests – not all of them totally legitimate. A new, 21 year lease was signed in October that year. The royalty was to be 1/20th for the first seven years, 1/16th for the second seven years and 1/14th for the final seven years. In addition, there was an annual dead rent of £100, plus £5 for the right to work coal for a steam engine which it was proposed to build at Cat Shaft.

In February 1882, Cookson transferred his lease to the Yorkshire Lead Mines Ltd, which had been incorporated to work the Hurst mines. Its nominal share capital was £65,000 and the following were listed as its first directors, each holding one share:-

T.M. Roby	Wimbledon
Retired Captain	
A. North	Kingsbury
Accountant	
E.G. Fellowe	3-4 Great Winchester
Broker	Street Buildings
F.G. Fellowe	3 Budge Row
No occupation	
R.A. Burnell	Shepherds Bush
Commission Merchant	
J.E. Harding	Camberwell
Accountant	
A. Garrett	Walworth
Civil Engineer	

John Retallick, a Cornishman, was the resident agent.

By October 1882, some 2400 feet of the Old Water Level had been cleared and six shafts repaired to provide ventilation. Cat Shaft was being enlarged to 8 feet by 5 feet between timbers and cleared down to the Water Level at a depth of 40 fathoms. A 14 inch thick seam of coal had been found in the shaft and it was intended to work it for fuel for an 18 inch, high pressure, horizontal steam engine. This was used for pumping and winding, and was working by November 1883. Cat Shaft was conveniently placed for developing at least six veins from short crosscuts. Moreover, the '*Old Man*' had not had all the ore. There was a six inch rib of ore in one of the Hawkins Strings, which was between two and three feet wide, and it was expected to produce six tons of ore per fathom. A crosscut south, from the shaft bottom, cut Gutter String, which was three feet wide, and then Redshaft Vein after a further 150 feet. The '*Old Man*' workings on the latter had run in, however. At the same depth, but to the north, was another of the Hawkins Strings and, 150 feet further north, Woodgarth Vein.

At first there was little water to pump from Cat Shaft because most of it ran away down the 17th century Water Level. The engine there was used for raising rock to the surface, where it was tipped, but ore was lifted to Queen's Level and then trammed to the dressing floor at its mouth. A second, 14 inch, high pressure horizontal engine was installed at Cat Shaft in July 1885. This engine hoisted two skips, each holding half a ton, and left the first engine free for pumping as the shaft was deepened.

At first, the company could not afford to buy and erect the necessary machinery and so the ore could not be dressed. By 1887 the floors could deal with 200 tons per month, if there was enough water to allow 24 hour working. The equipment included two waterwheels, one of 31 feet and the other of 14 feet diameter; two crushing mills; three self-acting jiggers; elevators and three circular buddles. In June 1887, a Zennor Buddle began work and greatly improved the recovery of fine ore.

Cat Shaft chimney

Some of the mine's reservoirs were enlarged, but dressing was often hampered by water shortages. For example, at the end of April 1887 the mine had produced 180 tons of ore, of which 100 tons had been sold, but the dressing floors were stood for want of water. A drought that summer led to more delays. Later that year a semi-portable steam engine was being used to drive the crusher and other machinery on the dressing floor.

By January 1885, when 12s 6d had been called on each one pound share, the directors asked the shareholders to give them funds for sinking Cat Shaft another five fathoms and developing three veins to the north. Most of the money came from Townsend Kirkwood,

a lead smelter, who was taking responsibility for ensuring the regular despatch of ore from the mine, via Richmond, to Newcastle. These deliveries were expected to be at the rate of between 100 and 500 tons of ore per month, but it is likely that the target was seldom achieved.

The mine had its share of accidents too. One, involving Thomas Pounder aged 26, from near Gunnerside, happened the day before he was to marry in February 1887. He slipped from a ladder and fell to the bottom of the shaft. When his rescuers reached him, blood was oozing from his nose and ears and he had several other injuries. Pounder survived being lifted from the mine and was carried home, where he recovered after several months.

A report in the *Mining Journal*, in September 1886, claimed that large quantities of high grade ore, which were rich in silver, had been found. This boosted the share price, but it was almost certainly fraudulent.

Captain W.H. Williams, of the Van Mine in Montgomeryshire, viewed the Hurst Mines in April 1887 and commented that *"the tips around the various shafts at Hurst would definitely repay working and I saw more lead on the roads around Hurst than at some mines where thousands have been spent."* He also recommended that Pryes Level, which appears to have been standing idle, be driven up to drain the ground around Cat Shaft. In the meantime, however, the two engines at Cat Shaft were working well, but an extra boiler was needed and the foundations of the winder needed strengthening. The shaft was 50 fathoms deep and two 14 inch lifts of pumps had been installed to lift water to the Old Water Level. Nevertheless, a second, larger shaft would have to be sunk to house the bigger pumps which would be needed as the mine got deeper.

Ore was being raised between the 40 and 50 fathom levels. Here the vein, which had chert on its south side and limestone on the north, was virtually untouched by the 'Old Man'. Overhand stopes on Golden Shaft and Cleminson's Veins were producing well, and ore in the soles of the former looked promising for stopes from a future 60 fathom level. Redshaft Vein was, however, unproductive. In all, 44 men were working stopes, plus another 22 driving various levels. Four men were clearing the Old Water Level and four more were clearing Hodgson's Sump from Queen's Level down to Brown's Rulley Way in order to ventilate the western workings.

Work on Brown's New Engine Shaft began soon after Williams' visit. It was being sunk from the surface, but was intended to connect with Brown's Sump, which it did in October. The local press carried a report of the boiler being brought from Richmond to Hurst, which took 18 horses plus others to help on steep hills. The chimney and the engine house, along with the pumping and winding gear, were complete by November. By June 1888, Brown's Shaft was divided down to the Old Water Level, at 33 fathoms, and the skip road, ladderway and pump rods were in place. Sinking continued and by May 1889, with the shaft into the Underset Chert, an air compressor and rock drill had been installed to speed up the work.

The cost of this development had been too much for the Yorkshire Lead Mines Ltd, however, and in January 1889 a new company, called Hurst Lead Mines Ltd, was floated to replace it. The new company was also under-financed and the Directors ordered John Retallick, the manager, to stop the men stoping by the fathom and use the old system of payment for each bing of ore raised. They also began paying Morley's duty in undressed ore after he refused an extension to the term of the lease. In December the company went into receivership after J.T. Kirkwood petitioned the Chancery Court.

The Official Receiver, Thomas Wilkins, tried to keep the mine going, but found that the cost of pumping the deep workings was prohibitive. He suggested stopping the engines and, instead, driving up Pryes Level, but no money was forthcoming and so the mine closed at the end of April 1890.

An attempt to float a company called the Hurst Mines Syndicate failed later in 1890 and so ended the only major attempt to use steam engines on a Swaledale Mine, though there had, of course, been short-lived attempts at Little Moor Foot and the Fryerfold Incline.

The mines were idle until 1937, when the North Riding Lead Mining Company began clearing and repairing Pryes Level. At the old forehead, they began sinking a sump in order to try the vein, but all drilling was by hand and the going was slow. Waste rock was tipped down the old hydraulic engine sump. The new sump was soon overcome by water and abandoned, as was a rise which cut into waterlogged 'Old Man's' workings. A little chert was worked and sent off in an old waggon to Richmond station, but the mine was abandoned in 1939.

Marske Mines

Leslie Tyson's study of mining and smelting in Marske did much to improve our understanding of this area's complex history. Being on the eastern fringe of the Swaledale orefield, Marske has only a few, poor veins and so mining there was never significant. Nevertheless, Marske is important to our story because, at Clints, it had large reserves of timber and a constant water supply near land with little agricultural value. This made Clints an ideal site for a smelting mill, especially as, though distant from a large supply of ore, it was near the routes out of Swaledale.

Marske is split into five lesser manors, but, apart from Skelton on the west bank of Marske Beck, where bales have been found, there is no evidence that the Conyers family, as its 16th century manorial lords, were mining there. The family did, however, have mines in Arkengarthdale and at Grinton.

Joan, the daughter of the late William Conyers and heiress to the family's estates married Arthur Phillip and so, soon after 1583, when he took a lease of the Grinton Mines, he built a smelt mill on the east bank of Marske Beck, above Orgill Force, in the Manor of Clints. The site of the mill became known as Smelt Mill Close.

In order to raise cash, Phillip granted a 21 year lease of the mill, lead mines and land at Clints to Alderman Cuthbert Buckle, of London, in April 1589. The smelt mill was described as *"All that milne in Marske as aforesaid with two furnaces now in the tenure or occupation of Richard Willance"*. By an involved series of sub-leases, marriages and sales, Phillip's Mill was bought by Sir Timothy Hutton in 1605. Three years later it was described as *"the seat and soyle of the laite decayed lead mylne or smelting houses in the territories of Marske laite in the tenure of Richard Willance of Richmond, deceased"*.

The site of a second mill is revealed in a sale of land at Orgate to Robert Willance in 1614. It is not clear who built that mill, but for convenience Tyson called it Willance's Mill. When Willance died in 1616, his estates, including the mill, passed to his nephew, Brian Willance. The latter's daughter and heiress, Elizabeth, married Dr John Bathurst in 1635. He worked the Arkengarthdale Mines, first under the Commonwealth (1649 to 1653) and then under a lease from the Citizens of London from 1654. Ore was carried from shafts, chiefly around Windegg, via Gun Nest to Willance's Mill. Here, two smelters (Ralph Warde and John Taylor) were paid 10s 6d for each fother of lead they produced, plus 2d for weighing it. The mill's single ore-hearth burnt chopwood which was supplemented with a little coal. The wood was cut and dried in woods around Clints.

On the death of John Bathurst in 1659, the mines passed to his elder son, Charles, who was in poor health. The mines were, therefore, run by his brother, John. However, when Charles died without issue, the mines went to his nephew and godson, also called Charles, who was the son of his second brother Theodore.

Willance's Mill must have been working near its capacity because some of John Bathurst's ore was sent to Humphrey Wharton's Gilling Mill for smelting. With output from Arkengarthdale increasing, therefore, a third mill was built at Clints, probably by the second Charles Bathurst around 1700.

All three mills are shown on Richard Richardson's 1759 map of Clints. The oldest, or Phillip's, Mill is shown as a ruin, but the other two are in a plot of ground called Mill Spring. Willance's Mill, the higher of the two mills, is shown with two smoking chimneys. On its western end was an overshot waterwheel, which was served by a leat running from Marske Beck. It appears that the tail water from that wheel drove a smaller, undershot wheel at the front of the mill's eastern end. This probably drove the bellows for a slag-hearth.

Bathurst's Mill stood about 130 yards downstream and had a single chimney. It too had an overshot waterwheel which drove the bellows and was fed by a branch of the leat serving Willance's Mill. A note on the map records that "*here lead from Arkendale is smelted*".

After Charles Bathurst died in 1740, his estates were administered by Trustees, who kept the mines going but sold Clints to Charles Turner of Kirkleatham in 1761. Turner was the son of one of the trustees and so it is likely that the smelt mills continued working. In 1767, however, he sold Clints to Viscount Downe and it is likely that the mills had closed by then.

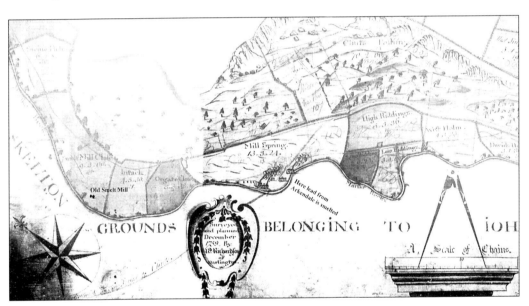

Smelt mills on Marske Beck at Clints

Lower Swaledale

This part of the valley is now more readily associated with farming than mining, but there have been trials on the strings which outcrop in the Main Limestone and Cherts between Downholme and Thorpe Edge, and at Feldom.

DOWNHOLME

The four principal mines, on veins at Downholme, White Earth, West Wood and Thorpe Edge, were worked between the 17th and 19th centuries, but some workings may be much older. In 1396, for example, Thomas De Percy had permission to dig for lead in his field, and three bales, which confirm lead production in mediæval times, have been found around SE116994. Much of the high ground immediately to the east of the lead mines is part of a military training area, on which there are numerous shallow coal pits.

The first mine, in Downholme village, is a level driven onto a fault running east-north-east in the Richmond Chert, but the absence of minerals on the hillock suggests that little, if any, ore was found.

At White Earth, two short, east-to-west veins, which converge as they run eastwards, have been worked by opencast and hushing. A level has also tried these veins in the Main Limestone, where they carried calcite, barytes and some galena.

High Spring Vein, which runs east to west through Red Scar in West Wood, was worked by a deep and wide opencut. It is also associated with a swarm of strings, or possibly flots, which have been tried from over 60 closely-spaced shafts on its south-east side. Their hillocks are mostly limestone and chert, with a little calcite and barytes.

Thorpe Edge Vein, which runs south-south-west, also shows signs of being associated with flots on the south side of Thorpe Edge Plantation, where it has been worked by randomly scattered shafts. Another vein, which runs at right angles through Thorpe Edge Plantation, has been worked by shafts, hushing and a level into the Main Limestone.

Sir Thomas Wharton of Edlington, brother of Philip Lord Wharton, bought the manor of Ravensworth from the family of the lately deceased Leonard Robinson in April 1675. It included land at Ravensworth, Marske, Feldom, Whashton, Gayles, Dalton, West and East Applegarth and Gilling. It is possible that Wharton had already been involved in the mines there with Robinson because he very quickly leased the mines at Thorpe Edge to Philip Swale and Robert Barker. Wharton took a one-third share in the new venture, but later assigned one-third of it (1/9th of the whole) to Swale. One-third of Robert Barker's third share was held by the same group of 'Derbyshire Partners' described in the section on the Old Gang Mines.

Thorpe Edge was a failure, but an account for early 1681 mentions 86 pieces, or nearly five tons, of lead and proposes that *"a little further tryall be made and a little oare smelted that it may be better judged what worke to carry on"*. The trial seems to have been abandoned by 1687.

For almost 200 years, nothing is known of these mines, but it is likely that they were not totally ignored. In July 1865 John T.D.

Hutton leased the mines at Thorpe under Stone and Thorpe Moor to a group of Grinton miners. This lease was revoked in 1869, however, because they had not worked the mine regularly.

The manor of Downholme was acquired by the Powlett family of Castle Bolton and, in 1767, Harry Duke of Bolton leased a piece of mining ground there to David Bradbury and John Berwick for 21 years. Nothing else is known of their efforts.

In April 1803, Lord Bolton's Steward recorded the discovery of a string, probably High Spring Vein, at Red Scar opposite Marske. He described it as being from three to four inches wide *"with a good deal of ore"*. The reports for the next 2 years suggest a fair level of activity and in May 1805 refer to there being *"nearly 100 pieces of their duty lead either at Hull or on the river from Boroughbridge"*, suggesting a total output of from 25 to 30 tons.

The last mining at Downholme was between 1856 and 1864, when Thomas Siddale got four tons of lead and William Alderson got 18 hundredweights of lead.

No smelt mill is recorded at Downholme, but the cast-iron base of an ore-hearth was unearthed when a derelict outbuilding was demolished. It may be, therefore, that another early smelt mill remains to be discovered there.

WHASHTON SMELT MILL

This mill, which was built to serve a number of short-lived mines in the area, stood near Copper Mill Bridge on Sturdy House Lane. Its location is confirmed by a list of tenants, made in 1686, which records that *"There is a peece of bad way in the pasture neare the smelt mill cald the Spring Pasture in Robert Reeveley's farming"*. The same document also tells us that Reeveley's farm was in Whashton, where three other tenants were smelters. The latter men may, of course, just as easily have worked at Gilling Mill.

Leonard Robinson, Lord of the Manor of Ravensworth, built the mill between 1647 and 1671. He died around 1674 and his estate

was purchased by Sir Thomas Wharton in April 1675. Swale and Barker sent ore from Lord Wharton's mines on Barney Beck to be smelted at Whashton Mill between 1671 and 1674. This practice must have continued, because in May 1685, soon after Sir Thomas's death, Philip Swale advised Lord Wharton that *"what benefit [the mill] made, it was by thy favour, for there was no oare but from thy work to imploy it, and without imploy it was worth nothing, but would require charge to keep it in repayre"*. Swale also remarked that the mines in Thomas Wharton's estates *"have lost much money in tryall and given yet no encouragement"* and that the joint stock was reduced to around £30.

Smelting had been delayed by lack of water in July 1685, but a slag-hearth was being prepared to smelt *"the quantity of slag about the mill, which must be smelted there because the oare hath been smelted there that afforded that slag, and made Sir Thomas more profit than if the slag had beene smelted in his time would have been"*.

The mill probably closed soon after the above slags were smelted, but there was a brief revival in the early 18th century, when it was used for smelting copper ore from the Feldom Vein. This vein, which runs north-east over Feldom Moor in Marske, has been extensively worked for lead by shallow shafts. Near the boundary with Whashton, however, the mineralisation changes to include copper. In June 1728 Matthew Blackburne of Gales, in Kirkby Ravensworth, blacksmith, was indicted with breaking into the copper smelting mill at Whashton belonging to John Ward and John Appleby and stealing four iron bars worth 11d. It is likely, however, that this revival was brief.

GILLING SMELT MILL

Humphrey Wharton, who had mines at Grinton and Fremington, bought the Gillingwood estate near Richmond in 1609 and, soon afterwards, built his own smelt mill there. This mill stands at the foot of Leadmill

Lane, on the east bank of Smelt Mill Beck, and is overgrown with trees and scrub. The beck here forms the boundary between the townships of Gilling and Whashton.

There may have been trials for lead around Gilling, but the estate had no productive mines. Instead, the mill survived by smelting parcels of ore from Arkengarthdale, as well as from Wharton's mines at Grinton and Fremington. This is confirmed by the following evidence given in 1697, during a case about the ownership of the Grinton Mines.

> *"Thomas Pearson of Gilling, who worked at the mill there, knew James Crathorne and Clement Chamber who worked for Humphrey Wharton. Wharton sent his lead there and he had often heard his master at the mill say Grinton had the best lead brought to the mill."*

Thomas Wharton, Humphrey's son, died in 1641 and the Grinton Mines were confiscated during the Civil War. The mines were eventually returned to Humphrey Wharton's grandson, who was also called Humphrey, and he reserved the mill and nearby wood when he mortgaged his estates to Ronald Graham in 1658.

William Wharton, the owner of Gilling Smelt Mill and the last male heir of the line, died without issue in 1746 and his estate was split between his sisters. He was working mines in Fremington, but does not appear to have had an interest in the smelt mill there, and so was probably smelting his ore at Gilling. His heirs do not appear to have done much, if any, mining and mortgaged the mines in 1796. It is likely, therefore, that Gilling Mill probably closed between 1746 and 1796.

Gilling Mill was very near to Jagger Lane, which was the main pack horse route out of Swaledale, via Marske and across Aske Moor, to Hartforth. Dr Raistrick believed that lead from the AD Lessors' Mines was stored at the mill whilst *en route* to Stockton on Tees, but this is incorrect. From the late 17th century until the 1750s, when the carriers started going by way of Richmond, lead from the AD Mines, at least, was stored at Hartforth, which is at the northern end of Jagger Lane. This arrangement probably began when Philip Swale lived at Hartforth Hall.

The first edition OS Map, which was surveyed in 1854, shows the mill as an 'L' shaped ruin. Raistrick's plan of the mill shows

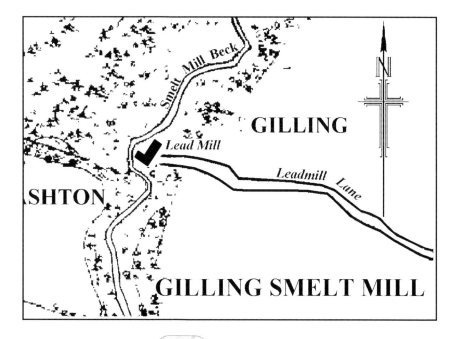

a number of internal divisions, but, in view of its overgrown nature, this should be viewed with caution. A roasting hearth is also unlikely in a mill of this period. The mill is more likely to have had one, possibly two, ore-hearths which could be used for smelting slag when enough had accumulated.

WAITWITH SMELT MILL

This was another early mill, in Hipswell, which had no apparent source of ore. Its precise location has not been fixed, but the first edition OS Map shows that part of Risedale Beck in Catterick Garrison, west of the A6136, as 'Lead Mill Beck'. Dr Raistrick placed it a little over half-a-mile downstream at Pleasant Dale.

Almost nothing is known of the mill's history except that it smelted some ore from Lord Wharton's mines in the early 1680s. It is likely to have had a very short life.

EASBY SMELT MILL

This, the least known mill in Swaledale, is shown on Jeffry's 1773 map of Yorkshire. The mill, near Brocken Brea Farm, is now the headquarters of the Brompton Caravan Park. There are no mines in Easby, however, and more research is needed to determine any links between local landowners and mines elsewhere.

The Parish Registers of Easby Church record various families living at the mill between 1741 and 1804, suggesting that it either had accommodation or had been converted to a dwelling by then.

Ashcroft, M.Y. (Ed) *Documents relating to the Swaledale Estates of Lord Wharton in the Sixteenth and Seventeenth Centuries* (Northallerton: North Yorkshire County Record Office, Publication No.36, 1984).

Ashcroft, M.Y. (Ed) *Papers of Sir William Chaytor (1771-1847)* (Northallerton: North Yorkshire County Record Office, Publication No.50, 1993).

Barker, J.L. "Bale Hills in Swaledale and Arkengarthdale" *British Mining* No.8 (1978), pp.49-54.

Barker, J.L. "The Mines of Downholme Moor and Thorpe Edge, Swaledale" *British Mining* No.48 (1993), pp.22-30.

Barker, J.L. & White, R.F. "Early Smelting in Swaledale: A Further Look" in Willies, L. & Cranstone, D. (Eds) *Boles and Smeltmills* (Historical Metallurgy Society Ltd, 1992), p.15-19.

Bassham, S. "Surrender Smelt Mill Flue" *British Mining* No.50 (1994), pp.161-168.

Berry, E.K. (Ed) *Swaledale Wills and Inventories 1522-1600* (Leeds: Yorkshire Archæological Society, Record Series, Vol.CLII, 1998).

Burt, R., Waite, P., Atkinson, M. & Burnley, R. *The Yorkshire Mineral Statistics 1845-1913* (Exeter: Department of Economic History, University of Exeter, 1982).

Clough, R.T. *The Lead Smelting Mills of the Yorkshire Dales* (Keighley: The author, 1962)

Dunham, K.C. and Wilson, A.A. *Geology of the Northern Pennine Orefield. Volume 2: Stainmore to Craven* (London: HMSO, 1985).

Fieldhouse, R. & Jennings, B. *A History of Richmond and Swaledale* (Phillimore, 1978)

Fleming, A. *Swaledale - Valley of the Wild River* (Edinburgh: Edinburgh University Press, 1998).

Gill, M.C. "Yorkshire Lead Mining - before 1700" *British Mining* No.37 (1988), pp.46-62.

Gill, M.C. "The Wharton Lead Mines in Swaledale" *The Local Historian*, Vol.18 No.3 (August 1988), pp.112-118.

Gill, M.C. "The Diffusion of Ore-hearth Smelting Techniques from Yorkshire to the Upper Mississippi Valley Lead Region" *British Mining* No.43 (1991), pp.118-128.

Gill, M.C. "An outline of the Chemistry of Lead Smelting" in Willies, L. & Cranstone, D. (Eds) *Boles and Smeltmills* (Historical Metallurgy Society Ltd, 1992), p.3.

Gill, M.C. "Yorkshire Smelting Mills: Part 1 - The Northern Dales" *British Mining* No.45 (1992), pp.111-150.

Gill, M.C. "Yorkshire Smelting Mills: Part 2 - The Southern Dales and Lancashire" *British Mining* No.48 (1993), pp.132-151.

Gill, M.C. "Yorkshire Smelting Mills, Part 3: Corrigenda" *British Mining* No.67 (2000), pp.108-119.

Gill, M.C. "Steam and Water Pressure Engines on Yorkshire Dales Mines" *British Mining* No.67 (2000), pp.70-98.

Goodchild, J. "The East Layton Copper Mine in Yorkshire and its Cost Book" *British Mining* No.48 (1993), pp.31-33.

Lodge, P.D. "Hydraulic Pumping and Winding Engines, Sir Francis Level, Swaledale" *Memoirs of the Northern Cavern & Mine Research Society* (December 1966), pp.21-26.

McNeil, J.H. "West Stonesdale Mine" *British Mining* No.19 (1980-82), pp.15-19.

Martell, H.M. & Gill, M.C. "Voyage Metallurgique en Angleterre (Ore Dressing)" *Bulletin of the Peak District Mines Historical Society*, Vol.10 No.5 (1989), pp.253-265.

Martell, H.M. & Gill, M.C. "Ore hearth smelting (Voyage Metallurgique en Angleterre)" *British Mining* No.41 (1990), pp.22-36.

Morris, D. *The Dalesmen of the Mississippi River* (York: Sessions, 1989).

Murphy, S. & Baldwin, H. "Early Lead Smelting Sites in the Swaledale area of Yorkshire" *Historical Metallurgy* Vol.35, No.1 (2001), pp.1-21.

Myers, J.O. & Whitaker, T.M. "The CB New Mill in Arkengarthdale - Some Photographic Evidence" *British Mining* No.48 (1993), pp.34-46.

Raistrick, A. *The Lead Industry of Wensleydale and Swaledale: Volume 1 The Mines* (Hartington: Moorland, 1975)

Raistrick, A. *The Lead Industry of Wensleydale and Swaledale: Volume 2 The Smelting Mills* (Hartington: Moorland, 1975)

Raistrick, A. *The Wharton Mines in Swaledale in the Seventeenth Century* (Northallerton: North Yorkshire County Record Office, Publication No.31, 1982).

Sharp, S. "The Alderson Lead Merchants and Pewterers of London" *British Mining* No.59 (1997), pp.75-78.

Smith, R. "Smeltmills of the Yorkshire Dales - The Grovebeck Mills" *British Mining* No.59 (1997), pp.108-122.

Smith, R. & Lamb, R. "Smeltmills of the Yorkshire Dales - Surrender Smelt Mill Flue and the Wilson & French Condenser" *British Mining* No.67 (2000), pp.5-25.

Smith, R. & Murphy, S. "The Jenkin Furnace at the New CB Mill, Arkengarthdale, Yorkshire" *British Mining* No.61 (1998), pp.91-100.

Tyson, L.O. *A History of the Manor and Lead Mines of Marrick, Swaledale* (Sheffield: British Mining No.38, 1989).

Tyson, L.O. "Mining and Smelting in the Marske Area, Swaledale" *British Mining* No.50 (1994), pp.24-40.

Tyson, L.O. *The Arkengarthdale Mines* (Keighley: British Mining No.53, 1995).

Tyson, L.O. & Gill, M.C. "The London Lead Company's Yorkshire Mines: A New Assessment" *British Mining* No.45 (1992), pp.151-161.

Tyson, L.O. & Spensley, I.M. with White, R.F. *The Grinton Mines* (Keighley: British Mining No.51, 1995).

White, R.F. "A Landscape of the Lead Industry: the Yorkshire Dales" in Palmer, M. and Neaverson, P. *Managing the Industrial Heritage* (Leicester: Leicester Archæology Monographs No.2, 1995), pp.61-66.

Willies, L. & Cranstone, D. (Eds) *Boles and Smeltmills* (Historical Metallurgy Society Ltd, 1992)

ARCHIVAL SOURCES

The following archival sources have been used.

The Brotherton Library at the University of Leeds – papers relating to the Marrick Priory mines.

Durham County Record Office – Hanby Holmes MSS for most of the areas covered.

Gateshead Library – Cotesworth MSS for the Hurst Mines.

Northern Mine Research Society Records – site reports, photographs and personal details.

North Yorkshire County Record Office – by far the major source for all the areas covered.

Oxford University Museum of Natural History – Smith collection relating to the dispute between the AD Lessors and the Aldersons.

Public Record Office – Crown Estate Papers for Grinton and Fremington, Chancery Masters' Exhibits and Board of Trade Records.

Warwickshire County Record Office – Shuckburgh MSS for the Old Gang area.

York Minster Library – Hailstone MSS for Arkengarthdale.

Yorkshire Dales National Park Authority – for a wide selection of site reports produced as part of its consolidation programme for lead mining monuments. Many of the photographs used in this book also came from this source.

GLOSSARY OF TERMS

Bale
A wind blown hearth, built on an exposed hillside, used for smelting lead ore in mediæval times. Bales were between three and six feet in diameter, surrounded by a low stone/earth wall and lined with clay.

Bing
Eight hundredweights of dressed ore, ready for smelting.

Bingstead
A storage place for dressed lead ore.

Bingtale
A system of piece-work in which miners were paid an agreed amount per bing, or part of a bing, of dressed ore raised. The mine owner deducted the cost of tramming (drawing) the ore from the mine, washing the ore, the candles and gunpowder used to get it, and any tools used or sharpened.

Bouse
Ore as it came from the mine (run-of-mine ore), mixed with rock and spar.

Bouse Team
A storage place for bouse.

Brouse
Partly smelted ore, produced in an ore-hearth.

Bucker
A small, flat-faced hammer used for crushing ore.

Buddle
A shallow channel, made from wood or stone and with a gently sloping floor used for treating the mixture of ore and stone which had passed through the sieve on a **hotching tub**. The mixture was placed at the head of the buddle and agitated in a stream of water, which carried off the lighter pieces and left behind the heavier ore.

Coe
A small, stone or sod building near or over the shaft top, used for storing ore, tools etc.

Cupola
See reverberatory furnace.

Daytale
Payment by the day worked. This was restricted to a few men, for example the blacksmith and joiner. Other one-off tasks, such as repairs, were also paid for in this way.

Durk Drift
A small dimension level, driven in the vein, often laid with a smaller gauge railway for getting ore from a **stope** to the main level.

Duty
A payment, usually a fixed fraction, between 1/5th and 1/8th, of the mine's output, made by the miners to the **Mineral Lord**.

Fathom
A unit of six feet, usually used for measuring depths.

Fathomtale

A system of piece-work in which miners were paid for the distance driven in a level or stope. The mine owner deducted the cost of tramming (drawing) the rock from the mine, the candles and gunpowder used by the miner, and any tools used or sharpened.

Flot (Float)

A horizontal ore deposit in which the mineralisation has replaced all or part of the original strata for some distance on either side of a vein. Flots are normally found in limestone, but a flot in sandstone is recorded at Apedale in Wensleydale. In the North Pennines, flots are called flats and can be very extensive.

Footwall

Where a vein slopes from the vertical (see **hade**), the footwall is the lowest or underlying side of the vein.

Fother (Fodder)

A variable unit of weight for lead. In Swaledale, the Stockton Fother, of 22 cwts or 2464 lbs, was favoured.

Galena

Lead ore (PbS – lead sulphide).

Hade

The angle that a vein made with the vertical.

Hand Level

A tunnel driven from a hillside, which was fitted with rails, but was too small for a horse to pull the waggons.

Hanging wall

Where a vein slopes from the vertical (see **hade**), the hanging wall is the higher or overlying side of the vein.

Horse Level

A tunnel, driven from a hillside, and usually rising at about 1 in 120, to provide drainage. Such levels were often specified to be six feet high and four feet wide and arched with stone wherever necessary — i.e. in soft rock.

Horse whim/gin

A horse-driven device for winding from shafts with a horizontal lever fixed to a rope drum on a vertical shaft, supported by a substantial wooden frame. The horse was harnessed to the lever and made to walk a circular path around the drum, winding the rope on or off as it went. Though the whims are long gone, their circular horse paths, many with a surrounding wall, can often still be seen, together with the large stone bearing-block, at the whim's centre, which supported the drum shaft.

Hotching tub

A wooden box, about two-thirds full of water, in which a sieve was suspended from the end of a long lever. A mixture of ore and rock, around the size of a coarse gravel, were put on the sieve and it was then jerked up and down in the water. This caused the material to separate, and any pieces smaller than 3/8ths of an inch passed through the sieve and collected in the tub (see **buddle**). The rock, being lightest, came to the top and was skimmed off and sent to the waste heap. Pieces of ore with rock attached to them formed a middle layer which was crushed smaller to separate them, and ore, being heaviest, formed a layer on the bottom next to the sieve and was sent to the smelt mill.

Hush

The process of clearing the soil etc from the outcrop of a vein by releasing a torrent of water from a reservoir on the high ground above. Hushing was also used to flush broken rock from opencast workings on outcropping veins. The resulting gash resulting from such work was also called a hush.

Jagger

Men and horses employed to carry the ore on the horses' backs from the mines to the smelt mill, or lead from the mills to market.

Knock-stone

A large, flat-topped stone, used as an anvil, on which ore was crushed.

Main Limestone
A bed of limestone, about 70 feet thick, from which most of the lead ore was raised. It was called the Great Limestone in the North Pennines.

Mark
Four hundred **pieces** of lead.

Meer
An ancient unit used for allocating mining ground along the length of a vein – in most of Yorkshire it was 30 yards long by 7$^1/_2$ yards (**Quarter Cord**) on either side of the vein.

Mineral Lord
The person, or persons, who owned the minerals, and from whom permission to mine them was sought.

Old Man
Former miners and their workings, of which no record remains.

Ore-hearth
A bellows-blown smelting furnace which was used at most Swaledale smelting mills. It burnt chopwood or peat, sometimes supplemented with a little coal.

Piece
An ingot of lead which weighed between 1 and 1$^1/_2$ cwts.

Pig Pan
The iron, or sometimes stone, mould in which pieces of lead were cast.

Quarter Cord
A quarter of a **meer**, usually 7$^1/_2$ yards in Yorkshire, measured on either side of the vein to give miners space for waste hillocks, piles of ore and any coe or building.

Rake
Usually a wide vein which had been worked from shallow shafts, i.e. Fryerfold Rake.

Reverberatory furnace
A coal-burning furnace in which the fire was kept separate from the ore.

Riddle
A sieve, often with a mesh of one-inch-square holes.

Roller crusher
Waterwheel-driven roller crushers were introduced at the close of the 18th century. A complete example can be seen at the Museum of Yorkshire Dales Lead Mining at Earby.

Rulley Way
See **durk drift**.

Shaft
A vertical, or near vertical, opening into a mine.

Slag-hearth
A bellows-blown shaft furnace which burnt coke and ran at high enough temperatures to melt slags and release any lead contained in them.

Stamps
These were made up of heavy poles, set vertically and shod with iron. They were lifted by cams on a shaft, which was rotated by a waterwheel, and then allowed to fall back onto an iron plate. Very hard ore, or slags, were placed on this anvil and crushed to a powder.

Stoping/Stope
The removal of vein-stuff to get the ore and leave behind a void called a stope.

Underset Limestone
A bed of limestone, about 24 feet thick and 10 fathoms below the Main Limestone, from which much lead ore was raised.

Water-blast
A ventilation device comprising of a long, vertical pipe down which a small flow of water was allowed to fall. The water sucked air with it as it fell and compressed it enough for it to be taken a moderate distance from the shaft bottom in pipes.

Windy King
A hand-worked, portable ventilation fan, usually turned by boys of between 8 and 10 years of age.

INDEX OF PLACES

INDEX OF PEOPLE & COMPANIES

LANDM▲RK COLLECTOR'S LIBRARY

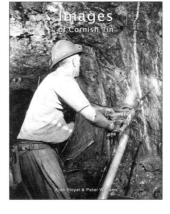
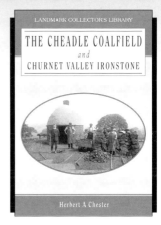
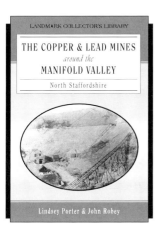
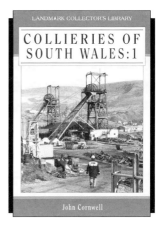